First man to orbit the earth.

America's first manned space flight.

Completed America's suborbital testing.

First day-long orbital flight.

First American in orbit.

Flight demonstrated man's adaptability to drifting flight.

Passed within three miles of Vostok IV.

First nation with two simultaneous manned space flights.

Increased American orbital duration.

Reentry control entirely manual, final Mercury flight.

Longest one-man orbital flight.

First woman to fly in space. Passed with

First three-man spacecraft.

CONTINUED ON BACK ENDPAPERS

*Gemini*

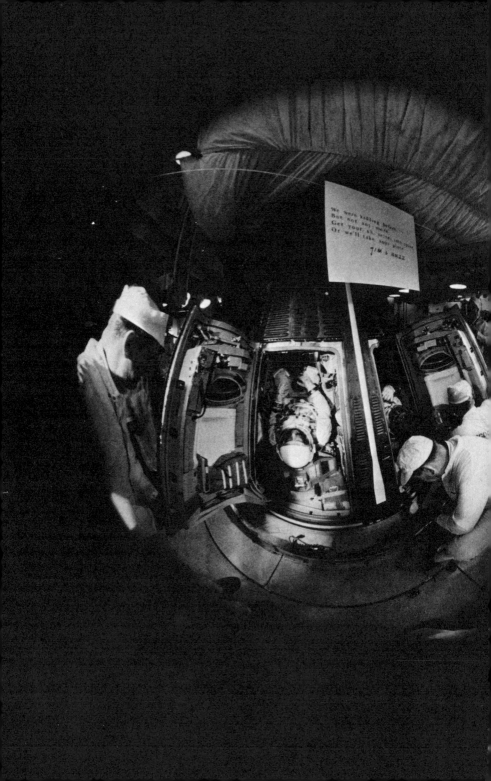

# GEMINI

## A PERSONAL ACCOUNT OF MAN'S VENTURE INTO SPACE

*Virgil "Gus" Grissom*

The Macmillan Company · New York
Collier-Macmillan Limited · London

The Macmillan Company, New York
Collier-Macmillan Canada Ltd., Toronto, Ontario

Printed in the United States of America

*To Betty, Scott, and Mark*

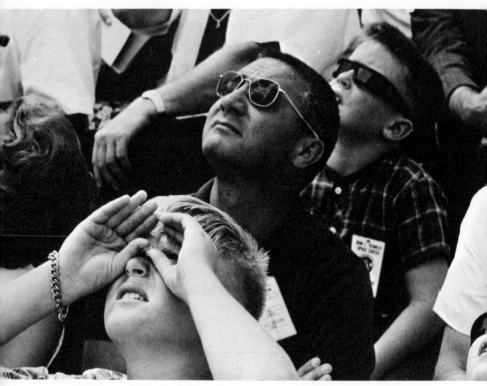

All eyes, including Gus Grissom's, stare into space, watching the launching of one of America's moon-probing rockets.
(World Book Encyclopedia Science Service, Inc.)

# Contents

# Introduction

Why would a man in my business write a book? The story is all there in the Mercury and Gemini technical reports, the computer punch cards, the endless miles of taped data; in the countless newspaper and magazine articles. So why a book?

Newspapers and magazines yellow and crumble away. And my two sons, Scott and Mark, may, like thousands of other young people, never learn to read a technical report or extract records from a computer's memory. Besides, computers don't ache with frustration, or relax over a long highball, grinning all over when something goes exactly right. Technical reports aren't concerned with the feelings of the people involved, just the results—did Gadget A operate on schedule? Did Gismo B malfunction? A computer wouldn't say that Gadget A worked because Wally Schirra sweated for weeks to be absolutely sure it *would* work when we needed it. It wouldn't say John Young [my copilot on Gemini 3] and I knew it would work, because we'd learned to have perfect confidence in our back-up team, Wally and Tom Stafford.

No, there's a lot that isn't on the record, and when they're old enough to really understand, I want Scott and Mark to know just what sort of weird, wonderful enterprise their father was lucky enough to have a part in fulfilling. I want them to know *why* there was Gemini in the first place, and what it was all about. I want them to share the friendships, the trusts, trials, and triumphs we've known.

That's why a book, or at least partly. Naturally, I'd like to see Scott and Mark follow my own lifelong interest in aeronautics and space, just as most of the doctors I know would be pleased to see their sons take up medicine. No job is worth having unless you've got pride in it, and I'm proud of mine, proud enough to enjoy the idea that my sons might pick it up where I finish. But my wife, Betty, and I aren't going to shove it down their throats. If Scott decides to become a deep-sea diver, and Mark decides he wants to be a chemist, that's fine, and we'll do all we can to see it works out that way.

Still I can't help hoping that maybe, just maybe, this book might swing them part of the way along toward what I think is the most exciting profession in the world. Or, if not Scott and Mark, some other youngster, just setting out to choose a career. Heaven knows, in the years ahead, once we've gone on from Gemini to Apollo and far beyond, we're going to need all the scientists and engineers and technicians we can get. So that's why a book, too. If this brings only one bright, curious, hard-driving youngster into space science and technology, that's justification enough for me.

This whole thing may come as sort of a jolt to the press crew who've covered our country's space programs from the beginning. To some of them I'm known as Gloomy Gus or the Great Stone Face, because I tend to clam up at press conferences. But trying to field questions from a bunch of hard-nosed, experienced reporters is a lot tougher than sitting down in front of a typewriter and writing to your own two sons, which is what I'm doing, no more, no less—yes, and to Walter Marty Schirra, III, and to little John Young, Jr., and even to Dionne and Karin Stafford, and Suzanne Schirra and Sandra Young, and all the other children of my colleagues in Gemini. This new dimension their fathers are just now starting to explore is going to need young women, too.

Mercury, Gemini, and Apollo are team efforts, to use a phrase long since hacked to death, and so, in many ways, it has been with this book. Every Gemini crew has come through with suggestions, and even better, criticism, just as they've done throughout the actual Gemini program. We've all worked together long enough to sound off if we don't like something or can figure out a better way to do it.

So here it is: the story of Gemini as we've lived it. There have been times when all of us have wished we'd gone in for some other line of work, say welding or psychology. Who hasn't? But when the first man touches down on the moon a few years from now, we'll know the whole thing has been more than worth it.

The Saturn V moon rocket blasted off its Cape Kennedy launching pad for the first time on November 9, 1967. The mightiest rocket ever launched will someday carry the first Americans to the moon. (W.B.E.S.S.)

# CHAPTER 1

## December 9, 1964

UNDER THE GUN is not a pleasant place to be, but on December 9, 1964, that is exactly where we stood with Project Gemini. My pilot, John Young, and I and our back-up team, Wally Schirra and Tom Stafford, were in the Mission Control Center (MCC) at Cape Kennedy. We were waiting for the launch of Gemini-Titan II-2 (GT-2), an unmanned spacecraft. The success of this unmanned flight would largely determine the fate of our own manned craft, GT-3, which was scheduled to be the next shot in the Gemini program. GT-2 was an exact replica of the GT-3 John Young and I would man—if GT-2 made it.

Things were particularly tense this December 9, and

wc were all feeling it. GT-2 had seemed to attract bad luck, and it was psychologically the worst possible time for our space program to run into annoying setbacks.

The last previous United States manned space flight had been Gordon Cooper's epic twenty-two-orbit mission of May 15, 1963, a year and a half earlier. But not so the Russians, our only rivals in space. One month after "Gordo" Cooper's flight, Russian cosmonaut Lieutenant Colonel Valery Bykovsky had flown eighty-one orbits in 119 hours and 6 minutes. And in that same month a Russian woman, Lieutenant Valentina Tereshkova, accomplished forty-eight orbits in seventy hours and fifty minutes. More recently *Vostok VII* had carried three Soviet cosmonauts aloft on a three-day mission, and the Russians were rightfully proud of their big spacecraft's "shirt-sleeve" environment and its capability for coming down on land.

Where were we in the meantime? Roughly two and a half years behind our estimated schedule, and at a cost of 1.3 billion dollars, more than twice the 600 million dollars originally named as the cost of Gemini.

The newspapers were asking hard questions and getting answers that didn't satisfy them one little bit. Now we were going to try to come up with some better answers, starting with GT-2, which had panned out a real hard-luck Nelly so far.

Just over a month after the big Titan II rocket, which would launch Gemini 2, had arrived at the Cape from the Martin Company's Baltimore division, in August, 1964, it was exposed to lightning strikes. This meant a schedule slip while it was checked out and its systems revalidated. Irritating, but not fatal.

Then later that same month along came hurricane Cleo,

and as a precaution the Titan's second stage was de-erected until Cleo blew herself into history. More delay.

A month later hurricane Dora began building up muscle out at sea. "If you thought Cleo was a honey, look out for this next one," the weathermen said. So on September 11 the entire vehicle was de-erected while Dora whistled past.

As a result it was October 6 before the Combined Systems Test, necessary before any flight, was completed, and only on November 5 was the Gemini 2 spacecraft mated to its launch vehicle.

It was no wonder, then, that public interest in this flight was close to zero. By this time I suspect some of the older hands among the Cape Kennedy press corps were figuring GT-2 would never get off the pad, and if it did, it would never go into orbit. The countdown was in its final hour, but the press site, more than a mile away from us at Mission Control, was occupied by a relatively small bunch of reporters, photographers, and television cameramen. During the Project Mercury flights the press site was usually packed with people, today there was plenty of room for the press corps to walk around while they waited.

The program they were probably betting would never happen called for GT-2 to travel some 2,150 miles down the United States Air Force Eastern Test Range, where a Navy recovery force lay. Maximum altitude would be approximately 106 miles, and the reentry speed would be 16,600 miles an hour. This would subject it to maximum heating conditions, far higher than our GT-3 would sustain.

Back at Mission Control John Young, Wally Schirra, Tom Stafford, and I waited, too. This flight was desperately important to us, not only because of its impact on the national program, but in a very personal way. If this flight were successful, it would be the go-ahead for John and me. When your whole life is bound up in a project like this, well, if you're not emotionally keyed up as the countdown moves along toward zero, you must not be entirely human. I know all four of us envied the "black boxes" that filled the pilot spaces of the spacecraft perched up there on top of Titan II. These were the two astro-robots, or crewmen simulators, with batteries for hearts, cameras for eyes, and other electronic gadgetry for brains and fingers. They would perform some of the jobs John and I were expected to accomplish on our manned flight. And their designers, unlike ours, had been considerate enough not to engineer them to worry.

But we were beginning to feel lucky. So far on this December 9 everything had checked out perfectly, with only a few brief holds. The beast which would give us the answers we needed stood 109 feet tall beside the towering gantry of Launch Complex 19, as the count trickled down from minutes to seconds. GT-2 was operating on its own internal power supply.

"T minus zero. Stage one ignition!"

Lift-off in three seconds! Back in Mission Control the roaring blast that was ignition sounded more like a low, muffled rumbling. Then the same unemotional voice: "Hard-over!"

It was like a karate chop behind the ear. Flight scrubbed! And nobody had to tell us. We knew. GT-2 would not fly this day.

Heaven knew what had gone wrong! And Heaven only knew how long it would take to find it, and if we *did* find it, how or even *if* it could be fixed.

Flight scrubbed! Gemini had slipped again. Poor America! Her spacemen had stumbled over their feet one more time. Gemini would probably still be on the pad when the Russians were launching commuter rockets to Mars.

Disappointed? Frustrated? That morning when GT-2 just sat there and went fizz, you can bet your life we were! But discouraged? It may sound ridiculous or like a whitewash job, but I honestly believe that December abort clobbered the press crowd much harder than it did the GT-3 team. Some of the newspapermen I ran into later that day offered me really sincere condolences, as if I'd just lost a dear relative. They weren't in a mood to kid about it. Neither was I, you understand, but I wasn't looking for a crying towel.

Consider it from our viewpoint, and you'll understand what I mean. As big a question mark as this setback had hung over our own GT-3 flight, there was another factor which affected us more directly.

It had taken just fifteen milliseconds for the Titan II Malfunction Detection System (MDS) to spot a drop in the hydraulic pressure of the number two engine's thrust-vector actuator. This had caused the actuator to shove the engine's thrust chamber to an acute angle. The MDS instantly switched to a back-up system, which steadied the engine in a neutral position.

It is National Aeronautics and Space Agency policy never to begin a flight when a secondary system is in operation. The Titan II was so circuited that if a secondary system were called on during the final three seconds, during which the big rocket was locked down to the launch pad while its engines built up to lift-off thrust, engine shutdown was automatic.

Now suppose John Young and I had been in that spacecraft, waiting for lift-off in those three seconds after ignition, and one of our engines had swung hard-over on its gymbals. What if the swing had *not* been detected?

Some people, they tell me, criticized NASA for including the extra weight and circuitry of a Malfunction Detection System in the Titan launch vehicle. They felt this was taking caution a step too far. But then these critics had the refreshing knowledge they wouldn't be up there in the Gemini spacecraft. That helps a whole heap when you're criticizing.

The fact is, that abort taught us something, as did everything else that happened in the Gemini program: Our MDS worked! Fifteen milliseconds isn't bad in anybody's league. A multimillion-dollar spacecraft and launch vehicle had been saved from possible destruction, and potentially, if not actually, the lives of two astronauts. All the checks and tests and simulations in the world could have given no better evidence that our MDS worked.

Astronauts tend to be firm believers in Murphy's Law —that's the one that holds that if anything can go wrong, it will! In this case it went wrong in the right place: on the ground, and not a hundred miles up at thousands of miles per hour.

December 9, 1964, wasn't a dead loss by any means. This is one of the few business I know in which failure means progress just about 99 per cent of the time. So you learn patience.

We were also learning that it's the process of preparing for a flight that is the toughest. It's sweating out what often seems like an endless succession of "glitches"—those Space Age descendents of the World War II "gremlins" —that creep into the works and gum them up beyond the capacity of man's reason to explain.

Yes, and part of it was keeping your temper when some cynical character asked, "Is this trip really necessary?"

Necessary? Absolutely! In fact vital. I can't presume to speak for everybody in the Gemini program, but I'd be willing to bet my bottom dollar that not one of us would have been in it if we hadn't believed in it wholeheartedly. And I think I know the basic reason we did believe in it.

Let me put it this way: If there had been no Mercury program, there would have been no Gemini program; if there had been no Gemini program, there could be no Apollo program, at least not within a meaningful time. If there were no Apollo program, it could well be that we would be handing on to the next generation a universe dominated by other powers, a world controlled from space, whether we liked it or not.

I don't want my two sons to inherit that kind of a world. It is as basic as that.

Yes, this trip was necessary!

CHAPTER 2

# The State of the Art:
# On the Way to the Moon

Put as simply as possible, the primary objective of Gemini was to advance the state of the art.

"The state of the art" is one of those phrases that usually annoy the daylights out of nontechnical people, especially coming, as this one does, from scientists and engineers who are supposed to deal only in precise facts and figures. I'm frank to say I don't know where the phrase originated, and I've heard numerous definitions, but in my book it means, "where we stand at the moment, what we know can be done because it has been done, and what we're pretty sure can be done in the future on the basis of the first two."

Technically *art* is the right word. There are still quite

a few aspects of space that don't, at the moment, seem to have any hard and fast scientific explanations. Sometimes a rocket will seem to defy all the laws of aerodynamics and simply break up for no apparent reason. Trial and error finally produce a mix that works, but nobody is quite sure *why* it works. Medicine still calls itself an art for the same reasons.

One of the best illustrations I've heard was a monologue by the television comedian Bob Newhart. It went something like this: It seems that a hot-shot Madison Avenue advertising man is on the telephone to Wilbur Wright the day after the first successful flight at Kitty Hawk. So the contraption will fly, will it? the adman asks.

Oh yes, Wilbur replies, it'll fly all right.

Carry more than one man? asks the adman.

Possibly, Wilbur concedes cautiously.

Say five or six or a dozen? the adman persists.

Also possible . . . maybe . . . someday, Wilbur admits.

And all those people will be lying stretched out on the wings? the adman asks incredulously.

Not necessarily, Wilbur says.

Well, declares the adman impatiently, all I want to know is where you're going to put the rest rooms.

That was the state of the art then, and its practitioners were as hard put to explain it to the layman as we are now.

Still, the state of the art was pretty well known, in broad terms, during Project Mercury. Everybody knew what Mercury was all about; that its objective was first to put a man in space, to see if he could survive there, and if he could, put him into earth orbit.

It cost me a ducking to help prove that man can survive

in space. Not only did Alan Shepard, our first astronaut in space, and I survive, we were able to make limited tests of our spacecraft's maneuverability.

Then John Glenn proved that man could take orbital flight, and importantly for the future, take control and actually fly his spacecraft. Speaking personally, despite the tremendous adventure involved in my relatively simple ballistic flight of *Liberty Bell 7*, I've always felt, as a test pilot, that man should not simply be along for the ride.

There are many decisions the little black boxes simply can not make, especially in the gray areas. To the little black boxes it is either *go* or *no-go*. If they'd been in complete charge when a signal indicated that the *Friendship 7*'s heat shield might be coming loose, John Glenn's flight might well have ended in disaster. The signal was false. John took charge, and that established man's function in space once and for all. There was a job for him to do, and only he could do it.

As early as May, 1961, President John F. Kennedy told Congress: "I believe we should go to the moon." Shortly thereafter, Project Apollo was set up as an official program of the National Aeronautics and Space Administration. At that stage of the game, it is worth remembering, man had to his credit just over two hours in space. Of that brief period, 108 minutes belonged to the Russian cosmonaut Major Yuri Gagarin in his *Vostok I*. The other fifteen minutes belonged to Al Shepard. What's more, anything the Russians had learned from Gagarin's flight they were keeping to themselves, so we could not learn from their experience.

Fifteen minutes is a pretty small fraction of the time it

will take to reach the moon, conduct any kind of meaningful research there, and return to earth. But in his address to Congress President Kennedy set us the goal of reaching the moon "before the decade is out."

Even as he spoke, while the Mercury program was still in progress, NASA's planners were thinking ahead toward the next step. They intended to call it Mercury II.

They were faced with a monumental question: What would the state of the art have to be in order to land a man on the moon? In 1961 the answers were far from encouraging, and the simple approach looked like the toughest of all. The "simple" approach required that we blast a spacecraft on a straightforward flight plan out of the earth's atmosphere, into space, and so on to the moon. After a reasonable period for limited exploration, the spacecraft would blast off for the return trip.

There was only one hitch to this brute strength solution. To do the job, the spacecraft would have to weigh somewhere in the vicinity of seventy-five tons. To ram this monster moonward would take a booster with a thrust of nearly fifteen million pounds! The Redstone rockets, which boosted Al Shepard and me into our suborbital flights, had a thrust of only seventy-eight thousand pounds. The Atlas booster used in later Mercury flights could churn out only up to three hundred and sixty thousand pounds.

The closest thing we had to fifteen million pounds of thrust was a concept. The concept was known as Nova. Nova would be a gigantic rocket, if it ever achieved reality, which was projected to develop twelve million pounds of thrust. But in 1962 Nova was little more than a gleam in the scientific eye. Even the most optimistic scientists felt it could never be readied in time for the President's target date. Clearly then, brute strength wasn't the answer

—at least, not yet: perhaps for the Russians; not for us.

You could say part of our problem was that we had out-smarted ourselves (you could also get an argument or two). We had had great successes in reducing the size of our missile warheads and guidance systems. Because of this the United States didn't need the huge rockets presumably required to accommodate the Russian warheads and guidance systems. We concentrated on sophistication, while the Russians went the sheer-power route.

Since the same rockets that carry warheads and guidance systems are also used to heave spacecraft into orbit, our highly sophisticated rockets left us without the brute force thrust power that from some points of view we needed at the moment.

Nova might someday be the best solution, if we waited for it long enough. But at the Marshall Space Flight Center in Huntsville, Alabama, Dr. Wernher von Braun and his team were developing the Saturn V booster, expected to be flight-ready by the late 1960's. Although it would develop only seven and a half million pounds of thrust, that would have to be good enough. This would mean a spacecraft of limited size and the use of a purely theoretical technique.

Instead of landing directly on the moon, the proposed Apollo spacecraft, with a three-man crew aboard, would simply go into moon orbit, letting gravity do the work of fuel, as it does in earth orbit. Then a two-man exploration vehicle, or Lunar Excursion Module (LEM), would separate from the mother ship and land on the moon. When its crew had carried out their mission there, they would re-enter their LEM, lift off with the small amount of fuel needed to overcome the moon's low gravity, and return to the mother ship, making a rendezvous in space. The LEM would then be jettisoned, after which the reunited trio of astronauts would return to earth and a much-needed bath.

That is how the problem stacked up in mid-1961. We hadn't even orbited the earth yet, but if we were going to hit our target date we had a lot to learn, and learn fast. We had to know whether man could survive the time-span of a return moon flight, whether he could first develop and then master the technique of making a rendezvous in space. If the answers turned out to be affirmative, then—and only then—would Project Apollo become possible.

If the two LEM astronauts were to return to their mother ship on their own, it seemed logical that the rendezvous technique should be developed as a two-man operation. If extended flights, possibly as long as two weeks, were contemplated, two men would be far better than one at performing all the in-flight experiments, and not at all incidentally, learning whether they could live together peaceably in such confined quarters for any length of time.

In the Titan I Intercontinental Ballistic Missile of the United States Air Force, NASA planners felt they just might have a booster capable of putting a two-man capsule into orbit. In the improved Titan II, with its four hundred and thirty thousand pounds of lift-off thrust, they were sure of it.

So, on December 7, 1961—twenty years to the day after Pearl Harbor, and four years, two months, and three days after *Sputnik I* became the world's first man-made satellite—Dr. Robert Gilruth, director of NASA's Manned Spacecraft Center, announced plans for the development of a two-man spacecraft.

Titan II flight testing was scheduled for early 1962, but no definite date was set for the first manned flight. The total cost for the twelve spacecraft, their boosters, and other equipment was initially estimated at $500,000,000.

A month later an official NASA christening named the program Gemini, after the constellation that includes the twin stars Castor and Pollux. The name was first suggested by Alex Nagy of NASA Headquarters, and it caught on overnight.

The birth of Gemini itself passed almost unnoticed. The giant project had made its appearance in this world amid the vast public excitement generated by John Glenn's flight and those that followed, by Scott Carpenter, Wally Schirra, and Gordon Cooper, bringing the Mercury program to its triumphant close early in 1963.

By this time those of us who had become involved with Gemini were beginning to suspect that we'd got, not twins, but a tiger by the tail. Kicking, screaming, digging in its heels, the state of the art seemed reluctant to have itself advanced. It always does. Happily for me, I have two growing sons who have also been known to kick, scream, and dig in their heels, so I was used to it.

# CHAPTER 3

## What Kind of Animal
## Is an Astronaut?

NOT LONG AGO I finished reading *Road to the Stars*, Major
Yuri Gagarin's memoirs of his career as a Russian cosmonaut. I got the distinct impression that the first time he
laid eyes on his spacecraft was the occasion of an unmanned test flight just prior to his own flight. I was left
with the feeling that he had had little or nothing to do
with its design.

If this was actually the case, it demonstrates a vast difference between the Russian way of doing things and our
own. In all our manned space programs we astronauts
have been deeply involved in every step of the development of our spacecraft and their supporting systems. If
one of us didn't like the solution the designers came up

with, we said so without hesitation. If we thought we had a better idea, we were free to say so, and often have.

Why didn't the scientists and engineers give us the old heave-ho when we sounded off? For one thing—and I mean this with all due humility—most of the time we pretty much knew what we were talking about. The reason we did was that all of us had had long experience as test pilots. They don't hand out PhD's in test piloting, but you pick up a tremendous amount of scientific and engineering knowledge along the way. After all, when you take up a brand new plane and put it through its paces to see if it will hang together, you are really flying somebody's theory. You have to understand that theory pretty well to check it out fully. Every new plane, every test flight, is a brand new challenge.

I suspect, this is why most of us became test pilots in the first place. Some flyers prefer to concentrate their skills on military tactics and the intricacies of combat flying. Others prefer the nine-to-five, home-for-dinner routine of transport flying, which gives a man far more chance for family life and the prospects of a comfortable retirement. And some of us are just plain curious. We want to find out more about flight, how and why it happens the way it does, how it can be improved. Even with luxury passenger planes and champagne dinners aloft, we still have a long way to go before flying becomes as safe as Mr. Otis's elevators.

Some science writers have criticized NASA for not including one or more scientists among the Gemini and Apollo flight crews. Undoubtedly this will eventually be done, and even now NASA is recruiting scientists for astronaut training, but at this stage of the game it seems to me that we're still in the testing phase. For example, the flight

John Young and I made in Gemini 3 was nothing more nor less than a test flight to check out the spacecraft, and I'm frank to say I wanted another test pilot with me, a man who could speak the same language, with the same kind of training and experience.

The best way I can possibly explain the background training and experience of an astronaut is to tell you about my own. It began back in Mitchell, Indiana, which is the kind of small midwestern town in which you would not be surprised to meet Penrod and Sam, small and unhurried. I was born there on April 3, 1926. I was the first of four Grissom children, including my brothers Norman and Lowell and my sister Wilma. My father, Dennis Grissom, worked for the Baltimore and Ohio Railroad, and while we were far from rich, we had a warm, comfortable family life, strongly reinforced by our parents' deep religious convictions. It's almost traditional in railroading families for the sons to follow in their father's footsteps, but Dad never made a big issue of this. In truth, he encouraged us to think about some other careers in which he felt there were better chances for getting ahead. I suppose I built my share of model airplanes, but I can't remember that I was a flying fanatic.

Nor was I much of a whiz in school, to be honest about it. I guess it was a case of drifting and not knowing what I wanted to make of myself. I'm reasonably certain that most of my teachers in high school didn't think I'd make it to college, or if I did, be able to keep up with the grades. My height was against me in high school baseball, but didn't keep me out of Mr. Robert Pingrie's Troop 46, Boy Scouts of America. A morning and evening paper route provided pocket money for Cokes at the Cargas Candy

Kitchen on Main Street, just across the street from the
*Mitchell Tribune*. Summers meant work and good exercise
in the orchards around town. If all of this sounds as American as blueberry pie, well, I guess it was, and I'll always
be grateful to Mitchell for making it like that.

And I'll always be grateful to Mitchell, Indiana, for my
wife, Betty. I met Betty Moore when she entered Mitchell
High School as a freshman, and that was it, period, ex-
clamation point! It was a quiet romance, as far as anyone
could see, but a special closeness started then and has developed into something several light years beyond the
power of mere words to describe.

The war in Europe seemed very far away from Indiana,
but we did read about the Stukas and the "few" of the
Royal Air Force Fighter Command. Certainly flying
sounded a lot more exciting than walking. Then came
Pearl Harbor, and I decided it would be the Air Force for
me as soon as I finished high school and could try to
qualify as an aviation cadet. My orders finally came
through in mid-1944, but the war ended before I got my
flight training. By this time Betty and I had married.

If it hadn't taught me to fly, the Air Force had taught
me that if I wanted to make anything of myself in aviation,
I'd have to go to college, and by now I was certain I
wanted to make my career in flying. Betty and I talked
it over and made up our minds. In the fall of 1946 I enrolled at Purdue University, at Lafayette, Indiana, as a
candidate for a degree in mechanical engineering. We
found a pint-sized apartment near the campus and set up
housekeeping. Betty landed a job as a long-distance telephone operator, and I found an after-class job as a short-
order cook, frying hamburgers for thirty hours a week, so

we didn't have much time for home life. By skipping summer vacations, I managed to catch up on all the courses I needed, and my degree came through in 1950. What I needed now was a job, and fast, because I didn't want Betty spending any more of her life at a switchboard. She had made my degree possible.

But I'd got the Air Force bee in my bonnet, and my job-hunting seemed to turn up nothing as exciting. My mother had it right when she later told a friend, "His heart just wasn't in it." So when an Air Force recruiting team visited Purdue, ex-Corporal Grissom was ready, willing, and able; and landed right back where he had been at the end of World War II, as an Air Cadet. Only the color of the uniform was different.

Betty stayed in Indiana while I completed training, first at Randolph Air Force Base in Texas, and later at Williams AFB in Arizona. There, six months after our first son, Scott, was born, she was finally able to join me on my $105-monthly salary. By that time I'm sure she must have felt that flying equaled poverty.

In March, 1951, Cadet Grissom became Second Lieutenant Grissom, I don't know which looked bigger, my wings or that salary boost up to $400 a month. We were practically millionaires!

Then, almost a year later in December 1951, came Korea, and one hundred combat missions with the 334th Fighter-Interceptor Squadron. (At about the same time the Navy's Wally Schirra was flying as an exchange pilot with the 154th USAF Fighter Bomber Squadron.) Returning home, I was assigned to the Air Force Institute of Technology at Wright-Patterson AFB in Ohio, and later to the Test Pilot School at Edwards AFB in California. This was what I wanted all along, and when I finished my studies and

The Grissom family—Scott, Mark, Betty and Gus. (W.B.E.S.S.)

began the job of testing jet aircraft, well, there wasn't a happier pilot in the Air Force.

Things were going fine, I figured, until the afternoon I wandered into the squadron operations office and the adjutant asked me, "Gus, what kind of hell have you been raising lately?"

"None that I know of," I told him, trying to think how I'd goofed, and when.

"It looks serious," the adjutant warned. Had I failed to salute some general? What was up?

"For Pete's sake, what is it?" I asked.

"Well, if you haven't been raising hell, who do you know in Washington? You must have some mighty important friends in the Pentagon, ole buddy."

By this time I was ready to climb the wall. "Look," I said, "I don't know a soul in Washington, and so far as I know I haven't been raising any hell, so come clean, what gives?"

In reply, he handed me a teletype message form, classified "Top Secret." It said that Captain Grissom would report to an address in Washington, D.C., by such and such an hour on such and such a date. What really intrigued me was the order that I should wear civilian clothing. By now I was as mystified as the adjutant, and the mystery wasn't much clarified by the instruction that I should discuss this assignment with no one. Just be there, and no questions asked.

Well, in the Air Force you get some weird orders, but you obey them, no matter what. On the appointed day, wearing my best civilian suit, and still still as baffled as ever, I turned up at the Washington address I'd been given. The first person I met was a quiet-spoken sort of guy who told me he was with one of the government security agencies. He said I would shortly be in a room with a number of other people. On no account was I to say what my job was. By now I was convinced that somehow or other I had wandered right into the middle of a James Bond novel.

Then they ushered me into a large reception room, filled with guys trying to make small talk, and all of us trying to look as if we did this sort of thing every day. But you can't get a bunch of pilots together without their figuring out what the other guy does for a living, and it began to be obvious that all of us were or had been jet test pilots.

They began interviewing us privately, asking all sorts of odd-ball questions, some technical, some personal, all of them searching. I still wasn't with it. Finally, though, they told me what it was all about. Nobody could order us into the space program; all of us could return to our regular assignments quietly, with nobody the wiser. But, it seemed, I had somehow met their requirements, and I was, as a result, "invited" to join the Mercury program. Don't give us your answer right now, they said. Think it over; see how your wife feels; then let us know.

I knew instantly that this was for me. This was where the future of test piloting lay. But they were right: It was only fair to see how Betty felt, although I think I could have told them then and there. Well, I went back home, and we discussed it, and as I had instinctively known, Betty agreed.

So began endless hours, days, weeks, and months of more rigorous training, studying, learning, than I'd ever been through before in my life. It paid off with my flight aboard the *Liberty Bell 7*.

Since I joined the United States Manned Space Flight

Program, several more groups of astronauts have been selected, including a number of civilians, but I suspect that my own background and experience are fairly typical of most of us, which is why I've included as much of it as I have. Some of us are products of the service academies. Others, like myself, come from civilian institutions. But all of us share at least one thing in common—the test pilot's unceasing itch to learn more more about flight.

# CHAPTER 4

# Elkton, Maryland: Space Age City

Now we've discussed how the astronaut functions in the space program, but the astronaut would have no function at all if he were the only, or even the major, part of that program.

What I found every bit as fascinating as the space hardware itself, with all its marvelous capabilities, were the people and places that combined to produce it. One of the most rewarding aspects of this astronaut business has been the chance to meet the men and women who were just as responsible for the success of the Gemini program as the pilots who flew the missions.

Only when you travel around visiting the various contractors who worked on Gemini do you begin to grasp the truly national scope of the program. It makes you more than a little humble, too, to realize, as I did, that all these people and communities are working to put you into orbit. And it can be more than a little surprising.

For example, Huntsville, Alabama, is generally thought of as "*Space Town, U.S.A.*" Houston doesn't blush a bit when people call it "*Space City,*" and Cape Kennedy is not the least modest about being "*America's Space Center.*" But what about Elkton, Maryland? Who would think of Cedar Rapids, Iowa, as a Space Age city? Or Paoli, Pennsylvania, Windsor Locks, Connecticut, or Hagerstown, Maryland?

Yet at Elkton, the Thiokol Chemical Corporation built our retro-rockets. In Cedar Rapids, the Collins Radio Company put together our spacecraft voice communications system, while in Paoli, the Burroughs Corporation made the ground-based computer for our launch vehicle radio guidance system. In Windsor Locks, the Hamilton Standard Division of the United Aircraft Corporation constructed ground servicing equipment, and at Hagerstown, the Fairchild-Stratos Corporation provided still other spacecraft necessities. And these are only a few of the scores upon scores of cities, towns, even villages that have become part of the Age of Space. I suspect that sometimes even the people living in them weren't aware of the part their communities played in Gemini.

All of us who flew in the program had some marvelous times visiting plants in dozens of these unadvertised space cities. In theory, some of our visits were for morale purposes—plant workers' morale, that is. In actuality, I think it probably did our own morale more good, because it gave us a chance to meet the people on whom, when you come right down to it, our lives depended.

Sometimes, though, we may have been of some help. I
recall one instance especially, because it produced some
fast action. It happened when Wally Schirra paused to
watch a highly skilled technician testing a piece of electronic circuitry. The man seemed to be taking a terribly
long time about it, and the longer Wally watched, the
more certain he became that that particular gismo wasn't
about to pass its test that day or any other day. So Wally
asked the technician why he simply didn't reject the
thing and pass on to the next.

"Because," the technician replied, "the form sheet I fill
out says I've got to go through all the steps, no matter
what, even if I can see that the part is no damn good."

"Why don't you talk to the foreman about it?" Wally
asked.

"Because I'd get fired, that's why," was the answer.

With that, Wally marched into the plant manager's office
and told him that a conscientious workman was taking too
much time because the poor guy was scared to talk to his
foreman. The form sheet for that particular test got itself
revised that same afternoon.

Time after time, too, we saw the men and women who
worked on our Gemini hardware come through in a bind,
when the chips were down. One instance stands out in
my mind. A major electronics contractor had assembled
a crack crew of about a dozen people to produce a guidance component. They finished the contract bang on time,
and as usually happened, the members of the team were
then reassigned to other jobs and scattered throughout
the plant. Much later, one tiny transistor, buried deep in
the guts of the guidance component, turned out to be
faulty. The only solution was to tear apart all the components built and replace the faulty transistors, which
could set Gemini back by months.

Somehow that contractor managed to reassemble the original production team—including one woman well along in her pregnancy—and they tore all those gadgets apart, replaced the faulty transistors, and put them all back together again in just over a week, as I remember.

With backing like that, how could we lose? If there's one thing I could wish, it would be that the neighbors of all those people who worked on our Gemini hardware could know that the fellow next door helped put this country a long step closer to the moon.

We found just the same pride and enthusiasm in the people we worked with, and are still working with at NASA. Many of them could make thousands of dollars a year more if they went into private industry, but they don't. They stick with it because they're totally committed to our space program and NASA, where the action is.

What I'm trying to say is that Gemini was more than nuts and bolts and sleek rockets. It was thousands of people, producing machines that did just about everything we asked of them.

If the four of us assigned to that first manned Gemini flight had ever needed rock-solid proof of the dedication of the scores of thousands of men and women involved in Gemini, we got it in the month that followed the December 9 abort. In that amazingly short time—as space development goes—the engineers of the Martin Company and the aerojet-General Corporation, builders of the Titan II's engines, had traced the malfunction and come up with a fix.

Failure, like the December 9 abort, takes a lot of explaining. Success doesn't need any explanation. So the end of the story of GT-2 is a short one. On January 19, 1965, the self-same GT-2 combination that had proved out its Malfunction Detection System the hard way lifted off on a 100 per cent perfect flight. Once again the four of us were gathered at Cape Kennedy, but this time there were nothing but broad grins as every system clicked.

There was no question about it: Gemini was moving again.

Gus and his co-pilot, John Young, waiting through the final countdown. (W.B.E.S.S.)

# CHAPTER 5

## Son of Mercury

I HAVE NOT, so far spent a lot of time telling about the actual Gemini flights. That is partly because you know that beautiful story as well as I do. It is also because, while the flights themselves get the lion's share of public attention, they are only a part of any space program—the final proof, the period at the end of the sentence. The stories I really want to tell here are some of the hundreds of tales that together make up the now historic volumes of Gemini. We've discussed some of the people involved and what makes astronauts tick, and we'll get to the fantastic hardware, the communications systems, and the recovery arrangements involved.

Now I want to look at how such a gigantic and almost

unbelievable thing as the Gemini program could come into existence in the first place.

To the best of my knowledge, the first suggestion that manned space flight might be feasible came in the mid-1950's from H. Julian Allen, a member of the National Advisory Council for Aeronautics, the predecessor of today's NASA. Everybody was in the ballistic missile race then, and Allen proposed to use an ICBM as the launch vehicle for a manned, high-drag reentry spacecraft. Nothing much came out of the suggestion, since ballistic missiles were still considered by the public almost entirely as weapons of war.

But in the scientific community the idea took hold, and in 1957 Maxime A. Faget, then of NASA and now Assistant Director for Research and Development at NASA's Manned Spacecraft Center near Houston, developed the basic design that eventually became the Mercury spacecraft.

The design was tailored to fit the lift capabilities of the Atlas ICBM—then our most powerful rocket—for orbital flight, and those of the less powerful Redstone Intermediate Range Ballistic Missile (IRBM) for sub-orbital missions. By 1958, given the impetus provided by the Russian *Sputnik I* and the creation of NASA, the concept of manned space flight had picked up tremendous momentum. On November 5, 1959, Project Mercury became official. At its head was an NACA veteran, Dr. Robert R. Gilruth, now Director of the Manned Spacecraft Center. Developmental work was carried out at Langley and Lewis Research Centers, and early test flights were scheduled at Wallops Island, off Virginia's segment of the Delmarva Peninsula. At the same time, planning was under way for a global tracking and communications network to support future orbital flights.

Nobody seemed quite certain what to call our first space cabin: Was it a spacecraft or was it a capsule? Initially *capsule* had the edge, since the funnel-shaped, 3,000-pound cabin was designed to do little more than provide a life-supporting environment in space for at least twenty-four hours for one man, who would be little more than a passenger and almost as useful as a baby in an incubator. Interestingly and significantly, the confusion persisted until John Young and I actually maneuvered our Gemini 3 capsule, after which the official terminology fell into line and *capsule* became *spacecraft* in the truest sense of the word. Capsule survives only in the term *Capcom*, the abbreviation for Capsule Communicator.

In an emergency, as John Glenn demonstrated, the pilot could override the controls, but only in flight. During the launch phase what was called an Abort Sensing and Implementation System picked up any launch vehicle malfunction and automatically ignited a solid fuel rocket atop a sixteen-foot escape tower mounted on the capsule's nose. This detached the capsule and pulled it up and away from the launch vehicle's explosive fuels. Following a normal launch, the tower would be jettisoned before going into orbit.

We first seven astronauts had been selected in April of 1959, before Mercury was announced, so we were able to participate in the basic design phase of the capsule we were to fly. Its interior was packed to the attic with little black boxes stacked in layers and backed into every nook and cranny. Sometimes this meant removing fifteen or twenty components when one failed, and in fact we sometimes spent two or three days trying to get one nut on one bolt, and the technicians had stiff arms and shoulders for days afterward.

Although some of the early boiler-plate, test-flight models were built by NASA technicians, the flight capsules were built by the McDonnell Aircraft Corporation at its sprawling plant in St. Louis. The first production flight capsule was delivered on April 12, 1960, just a year and two months after the initial contract had been signed.

Meantime the Western Electric Company was working on the worldwide ground tracking system, while the B. F. Goodrich Company, with its experience in putting together pressurized flight suits, had been selected to create the first Mercury space suit.

The first unmanned Mercury production capsule was launched from Wallops Island on May 9, 1960, in a perfect flight that proved out the complete escape, landing, and recovery systems. After that came a series of failures.

What happened was only natural. What would have been eerie was a total lack of failures. NASA's scientists and engineers were developing not only a new kind of hardware, but a whole new technology as well, and all this against a tight time schedule. If the slide rules and computers couldn't come up with the answers, maybe trial and error could. In this country we like to point to our advanced automotive technology with its mass production, its automatic transmissions, power steering, and so on. But it has taken more than half a century to develop to its present status. NASA was fighting to develop an infinitely more sophisticated technology in half a decade, and did. People tend to forget that.

If the Russian triumph in producing man's first artificial satellite had finally snapped us out of our calm conviction

Soviet *Vostok* spacecraft on exhibit in Moscow, said to be the same type as flown by Major Yuri Gagarin. (Sovfoto)

that our rocket science was the world's best, Major Gagarin's orbital flight was a bitter reminder that we were still
behind. No one could recover the years we had wasted. In
comparison with the big Russian boosters, the Redstone
IRBM scheduled to launch the first American into space
seemed just about as powerful as a youngster's Fourth of
July Roman candle.

Now was the time to push the panic button, if anybody
in this country was going to do it. I'm sure a lot of private
citizens pushed their own private panic buttons, but no
one in authority did, a fact that still makes me proud.
Mercury would proceed on *our* schedule, not a hurry-
hurry job dictated by a cheap motive, trying to steal at
least a little of the Russian thunder.

Mercury was going along in full view of the world.
Every time we goofed, and we goofed as often as the next
fallible human being, the world knew about it, down to
which screw got loose in what part, and why, if we could
find that out. Our first manned flight would be covered
in even more detail by our own and the foreign press.
The Russians never operated this way, never conceded a
failure. Indeed, they carry their policy of secrecy to the
extent that in his memoirs, Major Gagarin refers to what
I assume to have been his back-up man only as "Cosmonaut Number Two," and the man I assume to have been
the mission controller as "The Theoretician of Cosmonau-
tics." (I wonder what Walt Williams, our Mercury Operations Director, would have done if we'd addressed him as
"The Theoretician of Astronautics." My guess is a fast
right to the chops.)

My point is this: Here in the United States a fatality in
this early stage of our manned space program, fully pub-
licized, could have done untold harm, especially if it

developed that an astronaut had been lost because his spacecraft and launch vehicle had not been fully checked. As a result, NASA was determined to stand by its original test schedule, to be as sure as it was possible to be that when the first American went into space he would come back safely.

On March 24, 1961, Redstone qualified for manned flight with a 115-mile-long junket, carrying a previously flown capsule. But before Redstone carried a man on a suborbital flight, there remained the orbital testing of the Mercury-Atlas combination. The capsule had not yet been checked out in orbital environment, and the recovery forces still had to go through actual postorbital flight drill. The Cape Canaveral launch officials and technicians in charge of the flight had "flown" only simulations.

The big day for Mercury-Atlas III-3 (MA-3) was set for April 25, with an astro-robot riding in the spacecraft pilot's seat. If ever a man had a grandstand seat for one of the most astonishing spectacles in the world, I did. My assignment for the day was to keep the big Atlas company as it gathered speed after lift-off. Flying a delta-wing F-106A, I was to approach MA-3 at 5,000 feet, ignite my afterburner, and climb up in a spiral alongside to observe this early phase of its flight. Gordon Cooper would take over from his 25,000-foot level and continue observation of the big bird.

Everything seemed to go perfectly on launch day. To allow me more observation time, it was decided I should go in at about 1,000 feet, keeping about half a mile distant from MA-3 after lift-off. No sweat. Ignition and lift-off were bang on schedule, and I was congratulating myself on having the finest possible view of an ascending rocket a man could hope to have. Afterburner on, and I was climbing alongside, watching each step of the lift-off sequence almost as if my mind had gone into slow motion. Numbly I saw the escape tower pull the Mercury capsule free of the Atlas, and then—*Kablooie!*

The biggest fireball I ever want to see!

Reacting automatically, without really thinking, I pulled up and over and went away from that place fast. From the ground, they told me later, it looked as if I'd simply flown straight into the fireball. A doctor friend of mine, who'd been watching from Cocoa Beach, told me he turned to his wife and said, "Well, now there are only six astronauts."

Scared? You bet your life I was scared! Gordo had as close a call as I did and says he was just as scared when the bird blew up under his nose. Actually, neither of us suffered any damage to our planes, which was some kind of a miracle.

Just how big a miracle I realized when I flew down to see how the spacecraft was doing as it floated on its chute toward the water. I knew they'd want a report on this phase of the abort. I remember thinking, my gosh but these are big seagulls around here today. They were flying all around my plane. And *then* it hit me—these were no seagulls. They were chunks of the exploded Atlas, falling. Again, not one hit my plane, for which I am duly grateful. It was quite a spectacle, but never again, thanks.

Despite this Atlas setback, the first manned Mercury flight was set for May 2, 1961, with Alan Shepard scheduled to make the trip.

As I've mentioned before, you learn patience in the practice of astronautics—or you get an ulcer. The May 2 flight had to be scrubbed when heavy clouds moved in over the Cape and squalls were reported in the planned recovery area. As a result it was postponed until May 4, 1961, on which fine morning Al Shepard became the first United States astronaut in space.

The story of the remaining Mercury flights has been told a hundred times, including our own personal accounts in the book *We Seven*. To say that our lives were radically changed would not be wholly accurate. We were, after all, still deeply involved in training for future space flights, we still had our families, our hobbies, and sports. Of course, the seven of us had some wonderful moments— for an American citizen there can be no higher privilege than meeting his President, and return visits to our home towns were occasions none of us will ever forget.

But the really radical change came, I think, not so much in our lives as in the thinking of the American people with regard to man's place in space. When Mercury began, talk of going to the moon was still taken with more than a grain of salt. Worse, we were developing what could have become a real inferiority complex concerning our own ability to overcome the problems of "Space After Mercury," though people were no longer saying, "We'll never catch up."

Most importantly for the immediate future, Mercury gave us a proven spacecraft design, which was a tremendous leg up for Gemini. No two Mercury capsules were exactly alike, but by the time of Gordon Cooper's final Mercury flight we had a pretty sound idea of what we wanted to keep, what needed further improvement, and what we wanted to add, and the success of the Gemini spacecraft throughout proved the worth of Mercury's contributions.

From absolute scratch in 1958 to a man-rated, test-flown two-man spacecraft in just seven years is, I maintain, not

bad going. Compare the photographs of the 1900 auto-
mobiles with those of the 1908 models: structurally and
mechanically they were well-nigh identical. The resemblance between the Mercury capsule and the Gemini
spacecraft is almost entirely in external configuration, and
even that only to a limited degree. In all other respects
the Gemini spacecraft was truly second generation, and
a whale of a lot more sophisticated.

So you see, without Mercury, Gemini would literally
have been inconceivable. Gemini was truly the child of
Mercury, and just as every parent wishes for his child, it
went on to accomplish bigger and better things.

# CHAPTER 6

# Birth of a Craft

No QUESTION about it, the Gemini spacecraft was the answer to an imperative challenge. The thousands upon thousands of scientists, engineers, and technicians who created it deserve more praise and gratitude than I even know how to give them. In my book they did a magnificent job.

To understand the degree of perfection demanded at every stage in the development of the Gemini-Titan II combination, one must understand the term *man-rated*. Man-rating is one feature little known outside the program. My own translation of the phrase is: workmanship above and beyond the call of duty. Every Gemini astronaut who flew knew that every nut and bolt, every inch

of wire, every transistor, was the product of the finest
workmanship the United States could provide and had
met perhaps the toughest standards of inspection and
testing ever imposed. No Swiss chronometer ever faced
tougher challenges.

Just to illustrate, there was the "chaperone system." It
was probably easier to be a guardian angel than a Gemini
"chaperone." The way it worked was this: In the specifications of the Gemini spacecraft and its launch vehicle
NASA designated certain parts as critical. That did it.
Let's say it was something as simple as a toggle switch.
From prime contractor to subcontractor went the word.
Down at the Super-Duper Toggle Switch Company the
management would call in one of its brightest young
engineers, congratulate him, and tell him he was now a
chaperone. At this point, if he were married, the bright
young engineer should have resigned, because from there
on in that "critical" toggle switch was his wife, children,
and mother-in-law, all rolled up in one. He was totally
responsible. He could stop an assembly line, hold up production, and talk back to the chairman of the board if
one single toggle switch wasn't completely up to specifications. And when production was finished, he climbed
aboard the plane delivering the switches to the prime
contractor and saw to it in person that they arrived un-
damaged. If necessary, he'd travel all the way to Cape
Kennedy to make sure his switches were properly installed
and checked out.

It was that kind of attention to detail that gave all of
us so much confidence in our Gemini-Titan combination.

Getting back to the Gemini spacecraft, the goal was to
come up with a vehicle capable of supporting two men

in orbit while they performed experiments necessary to the success of Apollo. These experiments would produce the answers to such questions as pilot reaction to long-term weightlessness, his ability to perform useful work outside the spacecraft, and his ability to rendezvous and dock with another spacecraft. Incidental to these would be the problems of in-flight meals, waste management, and space navigation.

The secondary objective was to come up with this spacecraft in time to be meaningful to the Apollo program. If, for instance, rendezvous and docking had proved beyond our capability, the Apollo planners would have had to consider some other means of landing men on the moon or put the whole program in abeyance until we developed the Nova concept mentioned earlier.

It was this secondary goal that effectively eliminated the proposition of a whole new design for Gemini, which some thought would be a minimum requirement. The obvious solution was an enlarged and greatly refined Mercury. This could be developed by the time the Titan II ICBM was modified and man-rated for flight. But it was not merely a matter of adding inches to Mercury's size —not by a long shot. Far more maneuverability would be required for rendezvous and docking, and the important control loops would be closed by the crew, not electronic circuitry. Initially, too, it was hoped some kind of device could be developed for bringing the Gemini spacecraft back for a controlled land landing, but this hope wasn't realized and continues to be studied for possible future application.

Since the Gemini program included extravehicular activity (EVA), a new dual hatch system had to be devised, capable of being opened and closed from within the spacecraft, rather than blown off as it was in the Mercury capsule.

The Titan II launch vehicle, dictator of Gemini's weight, now laid down another  requirement. The fuels that propelled Atlas were highly explosive, so a disaster on the pad or during launch would convert the big rocket into a mass of flying shrapnel; thus the need for the escape tower and rocket to pull the Mercury capsule up and out of that shower of lethal metal. The Titan II's fuel, on the other hand, while combustible, was not explosive, and the consequence of an accident would be a fireball without the blast. Thus the heavy escape tower was not needed, and a type of ejection seat could be used for aborts on the pad and in early flight. The weight saved could be put to good use in the spacecraft.

With the experience gained in building the Mercury capsules, it was hardly surprising the McDonnell Aircraft Corporation was selected to build the Gemini spacecraft in January of 1962. What emerged from their vast plant in St. Louis some two years later reminded me of Oliver J. Dragon, of Burr Tilstrom's "Kukla, Fran and Ollie" television series. Viewed directly from the front, the Gemini's two hatch windows seem to give it an expression of ineffable melancholy, and the drooping nose could belong to nothing and nobody but Oliver J. Viewed from the side, it looks like a Mercury capsule that threw the diet rules away.*

Actually, the external dimensions of Gemini are about a foot longer and a foot wider than Mercury, making it

---

* You'll notice that I write about the Gemini spacecraft in the present tense, even though the program is complete. I suspect we haven't seen the last of them in space.

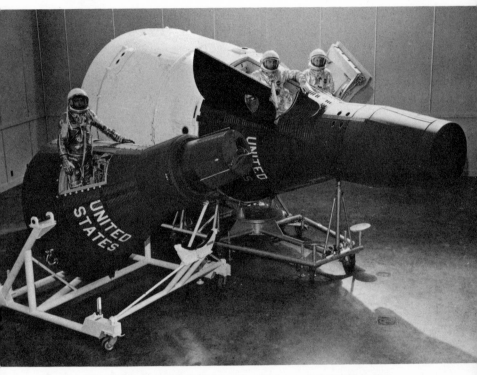

Mercury, the "Man in a Can" spacecraft which carried the first United States astronaut into space, foreground, contrasts with the Gemini and its adapter section aft, but the family resemblance remains. (NASA)

11 feet long (or high, depending on how you look at it) and 7 1/2 feet in diameter at the base. But this is only the reentry section, which is the only part of Gemini comparable to Mercury. This is the manned spacecraft, and it contains everything needed for lift-off, powered flight, reentry, and recovery, and while the size increase of this section may not seem like much, it gives the crew approximately 50 per cent more room inside.

The big difference in Gemini is its adapter module, astern, or below the reentry section. This stands 9 feet high, tapering from the 10-foot-diameter base required to mate with the Titan II. The adapter module itself is divided into two sections, the lower of which is the equipment section. This houses rockets for orbital maneuvering, an oxygen supply which can keep two men going for possibly four weeks, and batteries, conventional or fuel cell, for electrical power. Just before the crew begins the business of reentry it is jettisoned to expose the upper, or retro, section, containing the four solid-fuel retro-rockets. Once they have been fired to brake the spacecraft for reentry, this section too is blasted off to expose the reentry section's heat shield.

The elongated nose of the reentry section—it becomes the tail during the blunt-end forward descent from orbit —is known as the rendezvous and recovery module. In this are contained a radar set, primarily intended to pick up the target vehicle for rendezvous in docking flights, a rocket thruster system with eight nozzles for retro attitude and reentry control, and a parachute recovery system for the final descent to landing.

Inside the reentry section, in the pilot spaces, still more improvement is evident. The black boxes have gone, except for those directly connected with the crew, such as suit instrumentation. In Gemini most of them have been packaged as complete systems between the walls of the pressure cabin and the spacecraft's outer skin, with access by hatches in the skin. If a system breaks down, the appropriate hatch can be opened and the system replaced as a unit without hauling the crew out and turning the cabin upside down. What's more, there are fewer systems to go wrong, since many of them have been replaced by men's brains. (Even so, you understand, the Gemini flight crews didn't have room to play handball when things got dull.)

The first things you notice in the cabin are the crewmen's couches. Each of us had his own individual backboard and seat pan, specially molded to fit our body contours. During emergency escape they become ejection seats not unlike those used in high performance aircraft, and they were carefully designed to prevent any part of the body from coming in contact with the edges of the hatch during ejection. Either pilot can eject both seats at once by pulling up on individual lanyards, located between the legs. There is no automatic gadget to do it for us, and throughout the Gemini program the decision to abort was the command pilot's, but if he were out of action for some reason, the pilot could do the job.

The Gemini ejection system was designed to work anywhere from the pad up to fifteen thousand feet. During an off-the-pad abort, a rocket would eject the seat, at an angle of 15 degrees to the horizon, to an altitude of about five hundred feet and a distance of some one thousand feet from the booster, far enough to clear the maximum fireball to be expected. The occupant would then be parachuted to earth. For higher altitude ejection the seat incorporates a fifteen-minute oxygen supply and a drogue

Gemini Mission Simulator at Cape Kennedy, showing arrangement of hatches and Command Pilot's seat couch. (NASA)

stabilization device to prevent the occupant from spinning and so losing consciousness before he can open his main chute.

To continue with the potential emergency situation, above seventy thousand feet of altitude an abort would call for the crew to shut down the Titan II engines, detach the spacecraft from the booster, and descend by spacecraft parachute. If it then appeared, with the limited control available in this mode, that the spacecraft might be about to descend onto unfavorable terrain, the crew would eject themselves at the proper altitude and come down on their own chutes.

Returning to the Gemini cabin's interior, directly in front of each seat is a window. The total window area is a quarter less than in the Mercury capsule, but the overall design gives both astronauts better wide-angle vision, and the flat glass cuts down the refraction you get in curved glass. As it happens, I had a hand in checking this feature out when I flew an Apache-type light aircraft with its windows masked except for an area shaped like the Gemini window. No problems whatsoever.

In all there are three major instrumentation panels, and except for communications, attitude control, and flight director, there are no duplications. Nonetheless, both pilot and copilot can reach all the controls needed to handle the craft safely. The top of the center panel displays our suit instruments and the status of our life-support systems. The smaller control panels to the right and left and the overhead circuit-breaker panels are split according to the function of the crew. In Gemini the command pilot, seated on the left, is responsible for the controls for guidance and rendezvous maneuvers. The pilot, on the right, monitors the instruments connected with systems such as the on-board computer and the rendezvous radar and systems aboard the target vehicle.

There's a lot of human engineering in the Gemini instrument panels: Those giving us information on our safety are directly before us; those less critical are further from our straight-ahead vision. All in all a very businesslike, no-nonsense layout, and the only thing they didn't include is Muzak (as Gordo Cooper and Pete Conrad suggested, not at all in jest, after their long-duration flight in GT-5). And of course our instruments were engineered to keep us posted on the launch vehicle's performance until separation.

One of the most important advances over the Mercury capsule isn't visible in the Gemini spacecraft. This is its ability to be maneuvered not only in space but also *after* its howling reentry phase. After reentry the Mercury simply dropped like a stone until it reached parachute deployment altitude. The pilot's only control of it lay in firing his retro-rockets at the precise second over the precise spot. In Gemini the center of gravity has been shifted so that the heat shield is just off center as it meets the atmosphere, and the effect is to give the spacecraft just enough lift to permit the crew to lengthen their glide path up to 350-odd miles beyond the planned landing sight, or shorten it by 300 miles. Gemini can also be veered to either side of the reentry path by some 50 miles. If the spacecraft is headed for just the right splashdown area, with no need to extend or shorten the glide path, the crew can roll the spacecraft, at roughly two revolutions per minute, to counteract the built-in lift. It is this feature that accounted for some of the astonishingly accurate splashdowns during the Gemini program, when television cameras aboard the recovery carriers were actually able to pick up the spacecraft before they hit the water.

The Gemini space suit was a considerably more sophisticated refinement of the original Mercury suit, as were the suits worn for extravehicular activity later in the Gemini program.

Not that everything about our Gemini spacecraft was perfect, you understand. I was never really happy with the solution to the unavoidable problem of human waste disposal, but at least it was more satisfactory than a system of internal tubes suggested by some of the aerospace medics. All of us battled long and hard to win the anti-internal-tube argument, for no matter how you sterilize, there's always a possibility of infection in orbit, which is no place to pick up a bug. That's the reason all of our medical sensors were external. For their part, the medical people weren't really entirely happy over our 100 per cent oxygen supply. But neither were they all that happy with the Russian double-gas system, using oxygen and nitrogen and carrying with it the risk of the "bends" if the cabin loses pressure. As matters stand at the moment, the Gemini pure oxygen setup has been selected for Apollo, but we could get a breakthrough that would eliminate the medics' concern.

And all of us are agreed that our ejection system had some pretty hairy aspects. John Young, my pilot on GT-3, watched one test in which the hatch failed to open. The ejection seat powed straight through it, and John's comment later was, "One hell of a headache—but a short one!" I'm glad none of us had to use ejection seats, since I suspect that while they would have saved our lives, they would have given us quite a beating in the process.

One of the biggest problems we encountered during the design of the Gemini spacecraft was communication, which may sound odd to nontechnical people, but it's quite true.

To illustrate, let's say the engineers came up with some gismo about which we astronauts had our doubts. So Tom Stafford comes up with what most of us agree is a better idea. Tom then talks it over with the NASA project officer; tells him what he has in mind, and if the project officer agrees, he in turn contacts the project engineer of the prime contractor involved, and tells him *his* idea of what *he* understands Tom has in mind. Then the project engineer for the prime contractor, in *his* turn, tells the project officer of the appropriate subcontractor his idea of what the prime contractor's project officer's idea of what the NASA project officer's concept of Tom Stafford's idea really means. I hope you're still with me.

What sometimes came back up the ladder as hardware could surprise the daylights out of you, because it bore not the slightest resemblance to your original suggestion. It always reminded me of that game we used to play as kids, where you all sit in a big circle and a message is repeated around the circle. I suppose in this business it's unavoidable—Tom Stafford used to say it's all a matter of semantics—and the chain of command is necessary if any program is going to run in an orderly fashion. (I'm sure that what my son Mark means when he says "enough" ice cream is something entirely different from my own interpretation of the word.)

So far, I haven't said much about our Gemini spacecraft's rendezvous and docking capability, but this will probably be more understandable when we discuss the Agena target vehicle.

he sustainer can take over and give the spacecraft that
ecessary extra shove to put it into orbit.

Because the rocket engines at the base looked so small
o do such a big job, we in Gemini used to call them "fly-
ng fuel tanks," which is a fairly accurate description,
ome to think of it. In fact, the oxidizer and fuel tank
valls themselves formed most of our launch vehicles' outer
kin, or as the engineers put it, they were part of the load-
earing structure. Each stage contained two tanks, the
pper for the oxidizer, the lower for the fuel.

Each tank of our Titan II was domed at both ends and
oined together by short cylindrical sections called skirts.
Between the booster and sustainer stages was the inter-
tage section, which separated with the first stage.

Actually, the second stage sustainer engine started burn-
ng before separation—what's known as "fire-in-the-hole
taging"—and its exhaust was vented through ports in the
nterstage section. The vehicle's electronics rode in an
quipment bay between the second-stage oxidizer and fuel
anks. These systems included guidance, telemetry, de-
truct, and our malfunction detection system, Titan II's
nost significant modification for manned flight.

At the bottom of this flying fuel tank were the rocket
ngines of the booster stage, looking downright insignifi-
ant. But they're what it's all about.

So far I've stressed the aspect of pilot-decision in the
Gemini program. Even the MDS left the final decision to
he pilot—its job was to tell him what was going wrong
nd allow him to make up his own mind to abort or carry
n, using a back-up system. But there was one man who
ould override the pilot—the range safety officer. He alone
ould put our destruct system into operation, after first

CHAPTER 7

*A Place to Go
and a Way to Get There*

FOR ALL ITS splendid capabilities, on the ground there is
possibly nothing in this world so utterly useless as a fully
equipped, man-rated spacecraft. It is like one of those
hot sports cars Wally Schirra and Pete Conrad are so crazy
about—with no wheels! There is a tremendous potential
packed into it, but it is not going anyplace. To perform
at all, it must get into its own element, space, and the way
it gets there is by means of a launch vehicle. For Gemini
they picked a winner.

Not until you have stood beside one of those big beasts
do you begin to realize how difficult it is to think of the
launch vehicle as having a useful life of just six minutes,
give or take a few seconds—the time it takes to smoke a

Agena target vehicle, photographed from Gemini 11 spacecraft at approximately 75 feet distance. (NASA)

giving us a signal to eject or separate the spacecraft. Happily, he never had to make that signal.

Someday we'll probably work out some method of recovering these big launch vehicles for further use, possibly when we get enough thrust to carry the weight of a recovery system, which might utilize parachutes or retro-rockets or both.

The third major piece of hardware in the Gemini program was the Agena Target Vehicle, the unmanned spacecraft that gave us an object with which to rendezvous and then dock. The Agena and its Atlas launch vehicle had already piled up an impressive performance record, sending scientific payloads into space, and the Agena's builder, the Lockheed Missiles and Space Company, made the modifications required for its Gemini mission. These included a target docking adapter, a secondary propulsion system, and components of a command communications system, among other changes. Mated, the combination stands 104 feet tall, with a maximum diameter of 16 feet, at lift-off. In space the actual Agena target shrank to a length of 26 feet and a diameter of 5 feet.

What made the Agena a likely selection as the Gemini target vehicle is the capability of its engines to be restarted in space. This capability is inherent in its fuel and oxidizer, which like the Titan II's, are hypergolic, igniting on contact. In effect, you could describe the Agena, too, as a kind of gas station in orbit, for once docked with it, the Gemini crews could use the Agena's fuel to perform additional maneuvers, including changes of orbit.

The docking adapter was fitted to the front end of the Agena, and during lift-off was shielded by a streamlined nose cone (or shroud), jettisoned in orbit, although as

Tom Stafford and Gene Cernan discovered during their Gemini 9 mission, shrouds didn't always work that way. When Tom and Gene arrived at their rendezvous, they found the shroud still partially in place, looking, as Tom put it, "like an angry alligator."

On the whole, though, the Atlas-Agena combination proved to be a remarkably reliable part of the Gemini program and gave us a lot of new know-how and a great many insights concerning space navigation, not to mention the feasibility of building space stations using the EVA techniques we learned.

Now the Agena gave us a place to go and the Titan II was a way to get there, but while we were up there running around in space, somebody had to keep and "eye" on us. That somebody is Mission Control Center (MCC) and a worldwide tracking system. From the very beginning it was clear that the Mission Control Center and tracking network used for the Mercury program would not be adequate for the much more complicated Gemini flights. For the first three Gemini missions—two unmanned and the one John Young and I flew—improvements and modifications in the Mercury setup at Cape Kennedy proved sufficient. This was during the period NASA was building a new Mission Control Center at the Manned Spacecraft Center near Houston; one with the vastly greater capabilities necessary to handle complex missions.

This is the real heart of the whole operation that will eventually take us to the moon. It is responsible for the direction of the entire mission. It must issue guidance parameters to the spacecraft crew, and monitor the crew's guidance computations and use of fuel, while continuously evaluating crew and spacecraft systems performance and

capabilities. Finally, it has the job of directing recovery activities.

Over and above these massive chores, Mission Control is also charged with conducting flight simulations and training exercises. This last gives the boys at MCC a chance to dream up some real nightmares to throw at the flight crews in training, and they do it with gusto.

Communications for MCC are handled through the Goddard Space Flight Center in Maryland, near Washington, D.C., which does its huge job with 102,000 miles of teletype facilities; 51,000 miles of telephone circuits, and 8,000 miles of high-speed data circuits. Transmission rates over these various circuits can range from sixty teletyped words a minute to two thousand bits of radar data per second, which should give you some idea of the vast

The world's most powerful space tracking and communications instrument, part of the U.S. global network, is located in the high desert near Goldstone, California. It is 210 feet in diameter, weighs 8,000 tons. (NASA)

amount of information exchanged during a space flight. I never cease to be amazed when I see the typed transcripts of communications between the spacecraft, MCC, and the ground tracking stations. Stacked up, the Gemini transcripts would dwarf a giant, and they are only a small part of all the information exchanged between spacecraft and earth.

The Gemini tracking network included eighty-nine stations (three of them aboard ships and thirty-four of them overseas). Each station was capable of message, voice, and data communications.

Capcoms (Capsule Command Communicators) were assigned at eight of these stations. They could talk directly with the flight crews. Elsewhere, communications could be relayed from Cape Kennedy or Houston.

NASA computed our over-all Gemini tracking network at ten times the capability of the old Mercury network. This additional capability was used to its nth degree when it had to keep track of not one, but two spacecraft.

It is possible that the time will come when this world-wide network will become unnecessary, and spacecraft will be tracked by unmanned satellites. Until that day comes, it is mighty reassuring to know that back down there on earth they know where you are and what you are up to out in space. If you get into trouble, they will realize it in Houston almost as soon as you do.

To the television audiences who followed the Gemini flights, the Capcoms at such farflung places as Guaymas, Mexico, and Carnarvon, Australia, were only anonymous voices, speaking what often sounded like pure gibberish. To the flight crews they were good friends doing a tough job, for which all of us will always be grateful. It can get a little lonely out there.

CHAPTER 8

# The Astronauts Are Coming:
# By Land or by Sea?

WITH THE TREMENDOUS strides we're making in space, I'm
not sure how much longer the law that says what goes
up *must* come down will be valid. In any event it was
still very much in force during Gemini. The question was:
How?

Initially, during Mercury, a part of the answer had
been supplied by our national geography and available
resources. The United States has the Atlantic Ocean to
the east, the Pacific to the west. It has a navy capable of
deploying vast numbers of ships, planes, and men over
both oceans. Logically, then, the fastest and simplest approach was to have a returning spacecraft land at sea,
where its final minutes of descent could be tracked by

mobile, ship-borne radar, and its splashdown pinpointed.

But as we will see, this is an enormously expensive operation. Clearly, a spacecraft's capability of landing on solid ground—a land landing—would greatly reduce costs, not to mention freeing an important segment of the Navy for its primary job of defense in a world of increasing international tensions. However, the provision of this capability would take time, and time was what we didn't have, so land landing had to be a secondary objective. If it could be developed, well and good: If it couldn't, we always had our oceans.

Russia's geography, by the same token, made land-landing capability an imperative, especially in view of the Russian policy of strict secrecy concerning its space flights. The Arctic seas available to the Russians are inhospitable for water landings, to say the least. To have designated a landing zone in the Pacific would have required a fleet deployment in international waters that probably held little appeal to Russian naval authorities. (Of course, I'm speculating here.) Any passing United States cruiser might have paused to take in the show—and make notes.

Then too, with their bigger boosters, the Russians could send aloft a spacecraft large enough to contain the additional fuel and equipment needed for a land landing. We don't know all that much about their technique, but my guess would be that they come in on parachutes as we do, using rockets to brake and cushion the last few seconds before touchdown, much as the Apollo Lunar Excursion Module will do as it lands on the moon.

So both nations chose the first available system.

What kind of a land-landing system was envisioned for Gemini?

Initially there were high hopes for a device probably

best known as the Rogallo Wing, or paraglider, a concept originally dreamed up by that indefatigable genius, Leonardo da Vinci, and largely neglected until research scientist Francis M. Rogallo, now with NASA, began to study it, as far back as 1945. By 1948 his study was well enough along to warrant a patent application for a flexible-wing glider. The idea was that its inflatable fabric body should be stored folded in the spacecraft's nose until it was released, after reentry, at about fifty thousand feet, to inflate and deploy at forty thousand feet. It would then be controlled from the spacecraft, just as in an airplane, for the final landing, which would be made on skids, extended from the spacecraft after reentry.

In theory the supporting flexible wing would give the spacecraft all the aerodynamic capabilities needed, but to date theory has pretty stubbornly refused to translate into practice. As of this writing, it will require further development.

Also investigated as a potential land-landing device was the parasail, a maneuverable parachute, but as the series of successful water landings grew in number, emphasis on land landing diminished. So a land-landing capability was one of the few Gemini objectives, albeit a secondary one, that was not achieved.

The policy of water landing had almost as much effect on the Gemini spacecraft's design as did the environment of space itself. In space Gemini was in its element; afloat it was out of it, in an alien world which demanded such space nonessentials as waterproofing, and enough stability to allow the hatches to be opened without swamping the ship (and hopefully, at least a minimum of insurance against crew seasickness). A great many of its systems would have to keep right on functioning in this foreign element, perhaps for days. Provision had to be made for fast communication with the crew of swimmers who would attach the inflatable flotation collar designed to prevent the spacecraft sinking in a catastrophic situation, such as, say the removal of an injured crew in high seas. Quite apart from the lives of the astronauts, NASA would also lose the invaluable data to be derived from postflight testing of the spacecraft.

It's probably not exaggerating too much to say that the situation was roughly comparable to designing a flying submarine. Nonetheless, the solutions were found, although the Gemini spacecraft could never be described as what the Navy calls a good sea boat. A great cork, yes; a luxury yacht, no, as all of us can attest.

The sea landings added another phase to our training, as we simulated the checks and procedures we'd have to follow, once down: electrical power tests; communications and location-aid tests (Is anybody out there listening?); spacecraft integrity tests for leaks. Most importantly, we had to learn how to egress under all conditions, including underwater, which meant we also had to learn how fast and in what attitude a spacecraft sinks.

Meantime, building on the Mercury experience, NASA and the Navy were refining the elaborate recovery system of ships, planes, and communications which had already proven its worth. Plans and procedures were developed for every landing situation they could imagine. Landing areas were divided into two categories: planned, and contingency. The planned landing areas were further divided into launch-site landing areas, launch-abort (powered flight) landing areas, periodic emergency landing areas, and the nominal end-of-mission landing area. Any landing

Splash-down! (W.B.E.S.S.)

outside of one of the planned areas was to be considered a contingency landing.

This meant that our recovery fleet included vessels that ranged in size from amphibians to aircraft carriers. If we had to eject on the pad, we'd be picked up by a team of amphibians and small boats, working in conjunction with helicopters. If all went well, we'd be picked up by a carrier or destroyer.

The first recovery swimmer arrives on the scene from
his helicopter. (W.B.E.S.S.)

With the spacecraft's flotation collar attached and
his hatch open, the Command Pilot prepares to egress.
(W.B.E.S.S.)

Now of course in designing its destroyers, the Navy hadn't been expected to go into the spacecraft recovery business. As a result none of the destroyers assigned to the recovery fleet was equipped with a crane powerful enough to lift a Gemini spacecraft aboard, if that became necessary, as it might in a landing far from the primary recovery aircraft carrier. What evolved was something of an Erector Set solution: a crane that could be carried aboard disassembled, and erected or taken down in about four hours. While they were at it, the crane's designers made it strong enough to lift the thiry-six thousand pound Apollo spacecraft out of the water, which had been the idea all along. In action, the crane is mounted on the ship's fantail and is operated by just one man, an important fac-

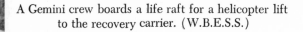

A Gemini crew boards a life raft for a helicopter lift
to the recovery carrier. (W.B.E.S.S.)

tor in reducing the difficulties of human coordination in rough-sea operations.

NASA and the Navy broke the whole recovery job down into three major tasks.

The first of these was location. This could be established by the use of tracking information from the Gemini network and high-frequency location-aid beacons aboard the spacecraft, radiating signals to be picked up by ground-based direction-finding stations. In addition, the spacecraft was equipped with an ultra-high-frequency location-aid beacon, which could radiate signals to the specially fitted airplanes assigned to all planned landing areas. This latter was considered the primary means of location-finding.

In a contingency situation, aircraft were so deployed at

bases around the world that they could reach any point along the ground track within eighteen hours of notification.

Visual location, once the aircraft homing was established, was assisted during daylight by a dye marker ejected from the spacecraft to spread over the sea's surface, and at night by a flashing light.

After location the second major task was that of on-the-spot assistance. This was provided by highly trained teams of swimmers. Each team was equipped with a flotation collar, and was prepared to give emergency aid to the spacecraft crew.

The third and final phase was the retrieval of the crew and spacecraft and their return to home base. The crews were given the option of remaining aboard their spacecraft or returning to the primary recovery ship by helicopter.

To accomplish the recovery mission, NASA and the Navy came up with a zone concept. The designated zones were the West Atlantic, the East Atlantic, the West Pacific, and the Mid-Pacific. Landing areas within these zones were established each time the spacecraft's ground track crossed the zone. The West Atlantic zone was established as the primary, or end-of-mission, landing area, and to it was assigned the primary recovery aircraft carrier and its planes, supported by destroyers. The other three secondary zones were covered by destroyers and oilers.

For our own Gemini 3 mission, the recovery fleet numbered seventeen ships. This number increased for later missions, but was not constant, varying according to the mission. All the services participated, including even the Marine Corps, with the Navy taking the brunt in terms of men and equipment.

By way of example, let's take a look at the Gemini 5

mission, flown by Gordon Cooper and Pete Conrad in August of 1965, and the forces deployed for their recovery. These forces were smaller than the preceding Gemini 4 recovery team, because by then NASA and the Department of Defense had gained enough experience to trim away unnecessary ships and planes, and the Gemini 5 recovery team became pretty much the model for all the succeeding Gemini missions. In all, 28 ships, 135 aircraft, and 10,000 people were involved.

At the launch site was a force of amphibians, motor launches, and helicopters, together with two armored personnel carriers capable of withstanding the heat of a fireball. Offshore there was a small fleet of navy minesweepers and a salvage vessel, in case the Gemini 5 spacecraft aborted, came down, and sank like a stone.

In the Western Atlantic zone was the aircraft carrier, USS *Lake Champlain,* with the destroyers *Dupont* and *New.* Aboard the carriers were search-and-rescue helicopters, in addition to the regular complement of planes, and a pararescue team.

In the Eastern Atlantic zone were a fleet oiler, the *Neosho,* and two destroyers, *James C. Owens* and *Manley,* supported by aircraft based at Bermuda, the Azores, and the Canaries, all carrying pararescue teams.

The Western Pacific zone, some 440 miles south southwest of Yokosuka, Japan, was covered by the destroyers *MacKenzie* and *Leonard F. Mason.* In the Mid-Pacific, about 500 miles north of Honolulu, were the oiler *Chipola* and the destroyers *Taylor* and *Goldsborough,* supported by aircraft and pararescue teams based at Singapore, Guam, Perth, Australia, the Samoan Islands, Hawaii, and California.

Contingency landing recovery forces were stationed at

Wheelus Air Force Base in Libya, at Aden, Mauritius, the Panama Canal Zone, Peru, and Rio de Janiero.

Backing this massive force were eighty-one doctors and medical technicians, posted around the world. At Pad 19, four general surgeons and eight technicians stood by to provide immediate emergency care in a disaster situation.

Aboard the Atlantic Ocean recovery ships were seven surgeons and three anesthesiologists; aboard ships in the Pacific sailed four surgeons and two anesthesiologists. At United States military hospitals around the world, speciality teams, briefed in bioastronautical medicine, were on the alert throughout the mission. And at tracking stations around the world, ten flight surgeons maintained a continuous monitor of the in-flight condition of Gordo and Pete.

In the highly unlikely event that a Gemini crew were faced with a catastrophic situation requiring them to come down on a land surface, they could have ridden the spacecraft down to parachute altitude, ejected for a normal parachute landing, and then hitch-hiked to the nearest telephone booth. Actually, this possibility was never lightly dismissed, and some of our toughest jungle and desert training was designed to cope with just such a pickle. By the time we finished, we could have come down in the Himalayans and milked the first yak we encountered, although I never did acquire a taste for jungle lizard broiled à la Grissom.

As Wally Schirra once put it to me, "It's a real nice feeling, knowing all those people are down there to pick you up, speaking as an astronaut. Speaking as a taxpayer, well, I wish it could be done cheaper."

cigarette. All that towering length of gleaming, stream-lined metal, all the beautiful precision of its intricate machinery and electronics, the product of thousands upon thousands of man-hours of work, will live for six minutes and then be lost forever.

That's what I used to think when I looked at the various Titan II launch vehicles being erected at Pad 19 to launch our Gemini spacecraft on their missions. (I also used to think how much better it was that these modified ICBM's were going peacefully into space and not toward some enemy target.)

Basically our Titan II launch vehicle was a two-stage, liquid-fueled rocket. One of its big advantages was that the fuel that powered the Titan was storable. Militarily this means that it's ready to go anytime, and doesn't have to have its propellants loaded just before launch. For us in Gemini it meant a considerably shorter prelaunch wait in the spacecraft, and this was a big morale factor. What you'd like to be able to do is kick the tires and go, and this was a step in that direction.

The propellants consist of the fuel itself and the oxidizer, which enables it to burn in airless space, and they are hypergolic, which is to say that they burn on contact and thus eliminate the need for a complicated ignition system.

The lower first stage is known as the booster and is roughly 71 feet tall, developing four hundred and thirty thousand pounds of thrust at sea level. The second, or sustainer, stage occupies the remainder of the Titan II's 90-foot over-all height and develops a thrust of one hundred thousand pounds at altitude. Briefly, the booster's job is to get the vehicle and its spacecraft off the ground and up to a speed sufficient to carry it to the altitude at which

Gemini-Titan II lift-off! (W.B.E.

# CHAPTER 9

# How to Make a Gemini Astronaut

WHEN MY MERCURY flight aboard the *Liberty Bell* capsule was completed, I felt reasonably certain, as the program was planned, that I wouldn't have a second space flight. By then Gemini was in the works, and I realized that if I were going to fly in space again, this was my opportunity, so I sort of drifted unobtrusively into taking more and more part in Gemini. What it amounted to, in fact, was that they just couldn't get rid of me, so they finally gave up and programmed me into Project Gemini.

I had thought training for Mercury was rigorous. Once we got caught up in the Gemini training program, our Mercury training looked pretty soft. Now we flew thousands of miles every month between aerospace factories

to watch them put our spacecraft and launch vehicles together, and between the training facilities, where almost
every phase of the manned flights can be simulated. The
days seemed to have forty-eight hours, the weeks fourteen
days, and still there was never enough time. We saw our
families just often enough to reassure our youngsters they
still had fathers.

There was good enough reason for this painstaking
training. We had a *lot* to learn! Not all the hardware in
the world, no matter how good it is, is of much use if
nobody knows how to use it.

The carpenter's apprentice must learn how to handle his
saws and hammers. The college engineering student
learns how to operate his slide rule long before he graduates. But how on earth do you train people for unearthly
jobs; jobs that never before existed, in an environment
man has never known? This was the problem faced by
NASA in training us to fly our spacecraft. And since we
in Gemini would actually be flying our spacecraft, rather
than, as in Mercury, simply going along for the ride, our
training had, of necessity, to be more complex, even more
intensive.

NASA also had to take into account the dangers of
overtraining—peaking and slumping—which apply equally
to astronauts as they do to athletes.

On top of all this there was the need for the astronauts
to be kept informed of the day-to-day developments and
changes taking place in the spacecraft and launch vehicle
and all the other aspects of space flight.

The object of the overall exercise, as Warren North,
chief of NASA's Flight Crew Support Division, once told
me, was to educate us to do scientific tasks and talk intelligently with PhD scientists in every field. A tall order.

(W.B.E.S.S.)

So, back to school we went. Our classroom courses included up to 160 hours of geology, 50 hours of flight mechanics, and 20 hours of math review, to cite just a few figures. Other subjects included astronomy, rocket propulsion, computers, aerodynamics, communications, physics of the upper atmosphere, guidance and navigation, selenology, environmental control, and global meteorology. If that sounds like the glamorous life, let me say it wasn't.

Following these came a series of science seminars in which we were privileged to do more than sit, listen, take notes, and ask the occasional question. In these we could really discuss theories and problems with some of the outstanding scientists in the country, men like Dr. James Van Allen, discoverer of the radiation belt named for him. To be able to talk what I hoped was sense to men of this stature in science, I know I studied harder than ever before in my life (even harder than the times I used to carry an engineering textbook along to my job as a hamburger cook, back at Purdue).

As our training continued, each of us was assigned an area of responsibilty for one or another aspect of space flight. The idea behind this was twofold. It engaged us directly in the engineering development program paralleling our training, and enabled us to keep abreast of what was happening and make suggestions when appropriate. So all of us became specialists of a sort in one field or another. No one astronaut could possibly keep up with everything that was happening, but he should have a general idea of the progress of the state of the art. To this end we held periodic briefing sessions, in which each of us could bring the others up to date in his own particular specialty, and answer questions afterward.

Survival training with life rafts for emergency landing at sea. (NASA)

This meant leaving the classroom for the factory floor or research laboratory, moving from brains to hardware so to speak. That gave us a morale-boosting change of pace and scene. It also added a course not listed in the official curriculum, public relations. On occasion, often without warning, we'd be asked to speak to employee gatherings, often impromptu affairs held right on the production line. I don't count myself a *summa cum laude* graduate of this informal course, but it taught John Young and Tom Stafford so much they joined Toastmasters International to keep in shape.

Someday, perhaps, an astronaut will be able to complete his training without ever leaving the Manned Spacecraft Center (MSC) near Houston. Not so for us. The Gemini training program carried us the length and breadth of the United States. A part of our astronomy training took place in the Morehead Planetarium, on the campus of the University of North Carolina at Chapel Hill. To accustom us to the G-forces we were to encounter during launch and reentry, we initially used the giant centrifuge at the Navy's Aviation Medical Acceleration Laboratory at Johnsville, Pennsylvania, near Philadelphia, later transferring this phase of training to the even more sophisticated setup completed at MSC during the program. Later, Extravehicular Activity training underwater was conducted in the enclosed swimming pool of a boys' school near Baltimore. There were spacecraft simulators at Cape Kennedy and at the McDonnell plant in St. Louis, and of course, those at MSC.

Our spacecraft simulators, designed and built to reproduce the conditions of actual space flight, insofar as possible on earth, can only be described as fantastic, and to me, not the least fantastic thing about them is that they were produced by men who have never been in space and probably have no intention of ever going there.

In those simulators Murphy's Law really got a workout. Every conceivable abort situation appears on your instruments, and you've got to react properly. Your cabin pressure drops; your fuel cells cut out; your guidance system breaks down; or your target vehicle acts up. And outside the simulator all of its associated computers are assessing your performance, catching every error, and you know all too well that after the simulation is over, you can't take the computers out and buy them a drink while you make excuses. Whenever possible, too, we suited up during our "flights" to increase the simulations' authenticity.

Additionally, all of us had some limited experience in actual weightlessness aboard an Air Force C-135 jet transport, flying parabolic curves. The technique is to put the plane into a steep power dive, then pull out into a steep climb which is eased into a huge arc. During a brief portion of this arc everything aboard becomes weightless for as long as thirty seconds. Early in the program it was hoped that effective EVA training could be accomplished in this fashion, but hard experience led to the later development of underwater training for the job, since it could continue for much longer periods in an environment that closely approximated weightlessness.

Over and above the academic and technical aspects there was survival training for contingency landings. I've mentioned our training for leaving a sinking spacecraft at sea and managing a liferaft. We spent other hours in desert country, looking like so many Bedouins in long johns—you can't walk a mile across a desert in a space suit, but a parachute makes a fine Arabian cloak and headpiece. We

Bedouins? No. Astronauts use parachutes as robes in desert survival training. What the passing train's passengers thought is not on record. (W.B.E.S.S.)

spent days in the jungles of Panama, and *that* was probably as bleak a time as any of us have experienced. Our other outdoor exercise came in the form of geological field trips.

The broad training program narrowed as the mission crews were selected, and as they concentrated all their efforts on their individual missions. So John Young and I, for example, concentrated on our Gemini spacecraft and its performance alone, for ours was really a test flight to see what the spacecraft could do, while Wally Schirra and Tom Stafford, going on the assumption that John and I would pass the spacecraft as flyable, hit the books on the techniques of rendezvous and docking.

Throughout our training NASA enabled us to maintain our regular flight proficiency by having us fly jet trainers and advanced fighter aircraft, on loan from the Air Force. Without these planes it would have been impossible to keep to our packed schedule, and I have, on occasion, breakfasted at Cape Kennedy, lunched in St. Louis, and had a late supper with Betty and the boys at our home in Seabrook, near MSC.

To give you some idea of the way the astronaut training program was interlocked with our participation in the Gemini engineering development program, I've asked Deke Slayton, who is assistant director of Flight Crew Operations, to allow me to reproduce our travel schedule for the period of April 13 through May 2, 1964. There's no particular reason for selecting this period, although it did give me a chance to visit Purdue, but it is, I think, reasonably typical.

April 13—All astronauts in Houston.
April 14—Suit molding at Weber Aircraft in Burbank, California. Astronaut Grissom.

April 14-16—Geology Field Trip to Alpine, Texas.
Astronauts Carpenter, Armstrong, Lovell, McDivitt,
White, See, Stafford, Schirra and Conrad.

April 15—Saturn Coordination at Marshall Space
Flight Center, Huntsville, Alabama. Astronaut Borman.

April 15-17—Gemini Coordination at McDonnell Aircraft, St. Louis. Astronauts Grissom and Young.

April 17—Astronaut Cooper will be at Flagstaff, Arizona, for a scientific meeting.

April 20-24—Four astronauts, unassigned, will be at
Langley Research Center for Rendezvous and
Docking Simulations.

April 21-24—Gemini Coordination at McDonnel Aircraft, St. Louis. Astronauts Schirra and Stafford.

April 27-May 2—Astronaut Cooper will be in Washington, D.C., for public appearance.

April 28-30—Ten astronauts, unassigned, will be at
North American Aviation, Downey, California, for
(Apollo) design review.

April 30—All available astronauts will be at Tucson,
Arizona, for a Geology Field Trip.

April 30—Astronaut Borman will be at the Martin
Company, Baltimore, for Zero-Defects visit.*

May 2—Astronaut Grissom will be at Purdue University for a public appearance.

That Purdue public appearance had nothing to do with
training or engineering development: It was part of that

* "Zero-Defects" was the highly effective program evolved by the Martin
Company to reduce production errors to an absolute minimum and
produce maximum quality control. Frank Borman's purpose was to tell
the Martin Company workers what a fine job they were doing in building our Titan II launch vehicles.

unannounced continuing course in public relations. My Alma Mater gave me the great honor of presenting me its Distinguished Alumni Award. It also gave me an opportunity to explain something about our aims in space, and this, I think, is tremendously important, even though I'm not much of a speechmaker. It is the people, after all, who are paying the freight for our space programs, and we have a responsibility to tell them how we're handling the cargo, even if it does sometimes put us into the position of looking like glamour boys.

I hope you didn't overlook that visit by ten astronauts to North American Aviation on April 28-30, more than six months before the first manned Gemini mission. Even while the McDonnell Company was working the bugs out of our Gemini spacecraft, the people at North American were developing the much more complex Apollo spacecraft, and through a continuing series of reviews such as this we were able to keep up with their progress. As we learned from the experiences of the Gemini flights, we were able to pass along our newly gained knowledge and suggest changes or improvements in Apollo systems.

It should come as no particular surprise to learn that the Apollo training program, while following the general outline of Gemini, will be more complex and demanding, especially in the area of navigation.

That our rigorous training paid off is proven by the fact that not one astronaut was killed during the Gemini space missions. Indeed, space was more hospitable to us than earth, for we lost three of our finest colleagues to accidents that couldn't have taken place in space. Ted Freeman died in an air crash during a routine training flight on October 31, 1964, while Elliott See and Chuck Bassett died when their jet smashed into a part of the

McDonnell plant as they came in for a landing at St. Louis on February 28, 1966.

All of us who flew the Gemini missions are pretty well agreed that the actual flights themselves seemed a lot easier than the simulations "flown" of the same missions on the ground.

Despite packed schedules and cross-country flights, we all managed to get in some time for our favorite sports, and gym facilities were available at most of our training centers for exercises and indoor games. Keeping in top physical condition was and remains a prime consideration for space flight.

This isn't to say we were a bunch of Rover Boys. When the rare occasion presented itself, we were all for a night out on the town at one of the many excellent restaurants at Cape Kennedy or in Houston, and it was a rare day that went by without someone bringing off a practical joke of one sort or another. This last was almost a tradition, and it may have begun with John Glenn's Mercury flight, when some joker (I have my suspicions) pasted a scrap of paper on John's instrument panel. It said, sternly, "No handball playing in here."

There was a final factor that, in my book, helped make the Gemini training program a success. Unlike our service colleagues in Vietnam, we were able to spend some time with our families in our homes. It wasn't all that much, you understand, but it sure helped to spend a quiet evening with your wife and children in your own living room after a couple of weeks of flying between training centers. The wives of the Gemini astronauts can take a lot of pride in and credit for putting their husbands into space. They had the courage, we had the know-how.

Then there was the wonderful, old-shoe treatment we

Rendezvous-docking simulator at NASA's Langley Research Center in Virginia. (NASA)

got at Cape Kennedy, at our homes, and in Houston. Strictly speaking, it wasn't really a part of our training, but it helped. There was no moviestar stuff, no stares, no special treatment, in spite of all the publicity the Gemini flights were getting. If John Young and I wanted to take in a new singing group at, say one of the Cape's motel dining rooms, we were just two more customers and nobody gave us a second look. We could relax and enjoy ourselves.

In closing out this description of our training program, I have to say that, of course, it wasn't perfect. No such program could possibly be, because you can't write a complete book of rules for a game that hasn't been invented yet. We were to learn from our missions a great many seemingly very simple things that had been completely overlooked when our training was set up, and this new knowledge has since been incorporated into the training of the Apollo astronauts. Some of the things that looked terribly difficult in training turned out to be easy, while some of the easy things proved impossible.

But that, as the advertising men are supposed to say, is the way the old ball bounces.

So now we've had a look at the hardware and the training required to operate it, and this seems like a logical place to say something about how the men who were trained for and flew the missions were selected. There was no magic about it, and nobody drew straws: The whole business was based on hard-nosed scientific calculations.

Although it has since been announced that a number of scientists will be selected for astronaut training for future missions, NASA stuck to its original Mercury specifications for the Gemini program. It decided that of all the jobs in the world, the jet test pilot's came closest to providing the skills and experience needed to operate a spacecraft. So we were all test pilots, military and civilian.

All of us were required to be United States citizens, with a degree in engineering or one of the physical sciences, and a maximum number of hours flown in jets. The increased size of the Gemini spacecraft raised the Mercury height limitation from 5 feet 11 inches, to 6 feet, which brought tall Tom Stafford into the program by the skin of his scalp, and the original under-forty age limit was eventually lowered to thirty-three.

The requirement for a degree in engineering or a physical science simply insured that the astronaut's education had set him up to understand the basics of space flight and spacecraft systems, and to be able to talk intelligently with scientists and engineers.

The experience in jet testing during the development of new aircraft would have prepared him to deal with the somewhat similar problems he might encounter in spacecraft, since each spacecraft is a modification or improvement of its predecessor, and modified procedures are required as a result. A test pilot, by the very nature of his work, is used to this sort of thing.

In 1963 astronaut qualification requirements set a minimum of a thousand hours of jet-pilot air time, or test pilot status acquired through the services, NASA, or private industry. Service membership was no longer mandatory, but a recommendation from the astronaut's parent organization, military or civilian, is necessary. Most of the Gemini astronauts had some three thousand hours of jet flight, with some of us having stacked up as much as 4,500 hours.

Once the physical, educational, and professional requirements were met, it was a matter of checking us out to see if our performance matched our records. There was a minimum of psychological testing. The very nature of our jobs pretty well precluded the possibility of selecting a psychotic. Test pilots who are mentally ill would not be likely to live long enough to rack up a thousand hours in jets.

It seems needless to say that we were all volunteers. Nobody, no matter what his qualifications, could be ordered to astronaut training.

Sooner or later, as our spacecraft grow larger, scientists designated as crew members may not have to undergo the full course of training, but will ride along purely as passengers with no responsibility for spacecraft operations. This, I think, will be a giant stride ahead, since there's little time for a flight crew to conduct experiments in space; a great many more could be made by a scientist whose sole responsibility they were. As the bus people say, he could leave the driving to us.

# CHAPTER 10

# Molly Brown

WE HAVE NOW taken a good look at the nuts and bolts that make up this stage of man's knowledge of space flight (the state of the art today); the men, the hardware, and the theories that were Project Gemini. Without some understanding of these components, any account of the Gemini flights would have been less than meaningful.

No two Gemini flights were alike, and each built upon the know-how gained by its predecessor, so each was a bit more sophisticated.

One of the most astonishing aspects of the Gemini program is the speed with which it was completed, between the flight of Gemini 3, on March 23, 1965, and the final

Gemini 11 mission on September 12, 1966; in just seventeen months and twelve days. That averages out to about one manned space flight every two months.

In the beginning no one could say with absolute certainty how long Gemini might take. Admittedly, the idea was to come up with the Apollo answers in time for a 1970 moon landing, but a serious failure in Gemini could have set us back indefinitely. Suppose, for instance, Frank Borman and Jim Lovell had returned from their fourteen-day Gemini 7 mission with serious medical and psychological problems; or there had been a disastrous discharge of static electricity during the first docking between a Gemini spacecraft and its target vehicle, despite the built-in precautions against that possibility. No one could estimate how long it might take to come up with the needed fixes.

A lot of the credit for Gemini's fast pace must go to the staff at Cape Kennedy, who demonstrated their enormous proficiency when the delayed Gemini 6 was launched toward its historic first space rendezvous in just under eight days after the launch of Gemini 7, which became the target vehicle. This performance amazed not only the press but us astronauts, who knew the prodigious amount of labor involved. Then too, they mastered the painfully difficult technique of the dual countdown and launches of target vehicle and spacecraft, which makes a Chinese fire drill look simple.

One result of our fast pace didn't really surprise me, but it was sort of amusing. When John Young and I returned from our Gemini 3 mission, there was hoop-la galore, to understate the case. Seventeen months later people were telephoning their television stations to complain that their favorite soap operas were being preempted for live coverage of the splashdown of Gemini 11. As my son Scott, would put it, "Crazy."

But this was no small part of the Gemini accomplishment. Space flight had been made to seem not only feasible, but almost routine, and not simply a kind of scientific freak. The swift competence of the Gemini launches, missions, and recoveries also informed the world that our space capabilities were in no way inferior to the Russians'. Despite our less powerful launch vehicles we had indeed found the answers involved in our own particular approach to a lunar mission.

Nonetheless, I'm afraid those irate television viewers were partly right. It is possible that a detailed review of each Gemini mission flown might prove repetitive. What I shall do, then, is give you the details of the mission I know best, the flight of Gemini 3. Many of the procedures John Young and I followed then became standard in the following flights, including the inevitable gags from the launch crews, the cheery preflight breakfasts, and suchlike. In following chapters I shall discuss the flights that followed ours, and I shall try to point out what each accomplished, how it was different, and why.

Over-all there were three basic types of Gemini flights: development, long-duration, and rendezvous-and-docking, with extravehicular activity figuring importantly in the last.

The developmental flights included the first two unmanned Gemini flights, and John Young's and my Gemini 3 mission. These were similar in nature to the kind of test flights flown in new airplanes here on earth. John and I were making a final checkout as human pilots of the

Gemini spacecraft, working with the data recorded by the black boxes on the previous, unmanned flights. Our job was to ascertain whether the black boxes were right or wrong. Just as importantly, black boxes don't feel discomfort or suffer inconvenience; they don't eat, and they aren't concerned with waste disposal. So John and I were not only concerned to discover whether our spacecraft was flyable; we also wanted to learn if it was livable. We were concerned with finding out how effective our life-support system really was. Could we certify our Gemini spacecraft as competent for the later, more complicated, and longer missions? It was no light responsibility, because those missions were going to be flown by our friends, and if we missed a malfunction or design flaw and turned over to them a defective spacecraft, we might be the cause of their death. We were also aware that if we found the Gemini to be seriously flawed and requiring extensive redesign, the whole program would come to a screeching halt for Heaven knew how long. As it turned out, Gemini 3 was the first and last manned development mission, since no more were required. Our spacecraft turned out to be a beauty.

The long-duration missions, Gemini 4, 5, and 7, were flown for the purpose of testing both men and spacecraft life-support systems, first for four days, then eight and finally fourteen, the last being the number of days estimated necessary for a return flight to the moon. There was a lot more than medical and technical knowledge involved; there was also the intriguing psychological question of whether two individuals, no matter how well adjusted, could live together in such confined quarters for so long a period.

Far and away the most complex were the rendezvous-

and-docking missions, Gemini 6, 8, 9, 10, 11, and 12, the
objective of which was to locate and dock with a target
vehicle in space, to prove the feasibility of a Lunar Excursion Module (LEM) returning to its Apollo mother ship
from the moon's surface. These missions involved highly
complex problems of orbital mechanics (incidentally, one
of the hairiest subjects I've ever studied) and extensive
spacecraft maneuvers of the greatest precision and del-
icacy. They also produced some of the most fabulous
photographs ever made.

When John and I were chosen for the first manned
Gemini flight, I began to give thought to what we ought
to call our spacecraft. During the Mercury program NASA
had given us the privilege of naming our own spacecraft,
and since there were only seven of us, all closely bound
together by reason of our profession and the training we
were sharing, the spacecraft names always included the
number 7: thus Alan Shepard's *Freedom 7* and my own
*Liberty Bell 7*. The practice followed the service tradition
of allowing pilots to choose their own names for their
planes.

In naming our Gemini 3 spacecraft, I always had in
mind the unfortunate fate of my *Liberty Bell 7*, which
sank like a stone when her hatch blew prematurely. I
nearly went down along with her. I owe my life to the neck
dam (a rubber collar) Wally Schirra had urged me to wear
so water couldn't fill my space suit and sink me.

At first I kind of liked the idea of using an Indian name,
say one of the tribes that once roamed around Indiana,
so I asked the research people at *World Book Encyclopedia* and *Life* magazine to see what names those tribes
had. They came up with the Wapashas, after whom the

Wabash River is named. Great, John and I agreed. We'd go into space aboard the *Wapasha*, a truly American name. Then some smart joker pointed out that surer than shooting, our spacecraft would be dubbed *The Wabash Cannon Ball*.

Well, my Dad was working for the Baltimore and Ohio Railroad, and I wasn't too sure just how he'd take to *The Wabash Cannon Ball*. How would he explain that one to his pals on the B&O?

At just about that time the Broadway musical comedy *The Unsinkable Molly Brown* was coming to its successful closing, and this gave me my clue. I'd been accused of being more than a little sensitive about the loss of my *Liberty Bell 7*, and it struck me that the best way to squelch this idea would be to kid it. And from what I knew about our Gemini spacecraft, I felt certain it would indeed be unsinkable. So John and I agreed that we'd christen our baby *Molly Brown*.

Some of my bosses were amused; some weren't.

"Come on, Gus, you can do better than that," the latter told me. "What's your second choice for a name?"

"Well," I replied, "what about the *Titanic?*"

Nobody was amused, so *Molly Brown* it was.

She was the first and last Gemini spacecraft to have her own name. Thereafter, the practice ceased. I guess they felt that the idea wasn't in keeping with the high scientific aims of our national space program, or maybe they were scared of what that incurable practical joker, Wally Schirra, might come up with when it came time for him to name *his* spacecraft.

Nevertheless there is a significance in the ending of this hand-me-down tradition from the services. NASA was letting us and the world know that Gemini wasn't a "Peanuts" cartoon strip episode, and we weren't a bunch of "Red Barons" flying around out there, dog-fighting in space. I was, naturally, a little sorry to see the practice come to an end, but I see NASA's point. Space is no place to be kidding around.

Since you'll be flying Gemini 3 with us, this would be a good place to introduce the people with whom you will be flying. They are my pilot, John Young, and our back-up team, Wally Schirra and Tom Stafford. John and I comprised what is known as the prime team, that is the team that is scheduled to make the flight. But if the prime team is incapacitated, the back-up team moves in to do the job. Anybody in our manned space program will tell you, a prime team can be no better than its back-up. Some people were under the mistaken impression that there was something second-string or junior varsity about the back-up teams, but this misconception vanished when Gemini 3's back-up team, Schirra and Stafford, went on to command their own flights. Indeed, Tom Stafford became the first back-up team command pilot to take over a mission, Gemini 9, following the deaths of the prime team, Elliot See and Chuck Bassett.

I like to call my partner in the Gemini 3 flight a city boy, since John was born in San Francisco in 1930, and raised in Orlando, Florida. A graduate of Georgia Tech, John is a navy man and a veteran test pilot. He alleges that when he was growing up, Orlando was really still a small town, but that's his story. John started out in the black-shoe Navy, and I never let him forget his destroyer days. After switching to flying, he set a world time-to-climb record in 1953, during Project High Jump. John says he got the flying bug at about the age of six, and his navy learnings from his father, who's a retired navy commander with World War II service in the Seabees.

John's not what you could call the talkative type, but he's got a good solid sense of humor, which is a prerequisite in this space business. Without one, you're in a bad way when the glitches come. And like the majority of us in the astronaut group, he's married. Barbara, his wife, shares her husband's dry wit, but where he draws cartoons, she writes, when she's not looking after their children, Sandra, and John, Jr. (Sandy and Johnny).

Wally Schirra, or to give him his full formal title, Captain Walter Schirra, Jr., USN, was the space veteran of our Gemini 3 group, with the nine-hour, thirteen minute flight of his *Sigma 7* Mercury spacecraft on October 3, 1962, during which he completed six orbits of the Earth. He claims to be a small town boy from Oradell, New Jersey, but if you check the map, you'll find that Oradell isn't much more than a hefty stone's throw from New York City, so I claim he's a city slicker with a Naval Academy polish. He is also, as I've mentioned, a sports car buff.

Wally saw combat duty in Korea before becoming a test pilot. He inherits his devotion to flying from his parents. The senior Schirra was a World War I ace, and after the war spent some time barnstorming the United States with Wally's mother before settling down to an engineering career. Like all of us on the Gemini 3 team, Wally is married and takes a proper father's pride in his children. Walter, III  and Suzanne (Marty and Suzy).

Like Wally, Tom Stafford is a Naval Academy graduate, but in Tom's case it was the Air Force that got the benefits of his Annapolis training. Like John Young he was one of the second group of astronauts selected in September of 1962 for space flight training. A native of Weatherford, Oklahoma, as is his wife, Faye, Tom was the only *bona fide* writer on our team, with two technical books on flying to his credit as coauthor. When he isn't studying, you'll usually find him making a fuss over his daughters, Dianne and Karin. And Tom was the only one of us who could lay claim to being a Harvard man: He'd just enrolled at Harvard's business school under Air Force auspices when he got word that he'd been selected for astronaut duty. He claims that when he finally retires, he's going straight back to Harvard.

So there you have the team that helped make Gemini 3 a success, and I think I can say we were a fairly typical crew in almost every respect.

Before Gemini 3, NASA was playing it very cool. Looking back over my notes, I find that at the beginning of 1965, for example, the most optimistic hope was that sometime during the Gemini 5 mission the pilot would simply open his hatch and stand up; nothing more ambitious was contemplated. But once John and I had discovered what a truly capable spacecraft we had, there was Gemini 4 pilot Ed White maneuvering himself on his tether, completely out of the cabin only a few months later, in June. And thereafter the pace never slowed for a second.

Briefly, our Gemini 3 mission called for us to exercise the spacecraft's orbit attitude and maneuver system—vital to the planned rendezvous and docking flights—and attempt a controlled reentry, using our on-board computer. The flight plan called for our Titan II launch vehicle to insert us into an 87-137 nautical mile elliptical orbit; that is to say the orbit's apogee, or high point, was to be 137 nautical miles distant from earth, and its perigee, or low

point, 87 nautical miles distant. After one orbit, at approximately first perigee, I was to operate our orbit attitude
and maneuver system to change the orbit to a nearly circular 87-90 nautical mile ellipse. On the completion of
two orbits, at approximately second perigee, we were to
maneuver again, to change the orbit into an 87-45 nautical
mile ellipse, with John operating our computer in conjunction with information telemetered from our ground network, to give me the times required for our controlled
reentry.

In comparison with some of the later missions ours
was what John Young would describe as "a piece of cake."
Still there was always that odd little feeling every test
pilot experiences each time he takes a new aircraft up
for the very first time; the knowledge that if something
goes to worms, it won't be you heading back to the old
drawing board.

But John and I had practically lived with our spacecraft
since the first rivet was put into it at the McDonnell plant.
We had studied every one of its systems as each was
installed, and sweated out the glitches along with the
McDonnell engineers. So we had the vital ingredient of
confidence going for us all the way. The same held true
for our Titan II.

I remember a reporter's astonishment at what he called
my "nonchalance" before the flight of Gemini 3. I assured
him it was not nonchalance at all, but the assurance that,
barring a total disaster, I knew our spacecraft was going
to work. It was as simple as that.

# CHAPTER 11

*Molly Flies*

AFTER NEARLY A YEAR of intensive training for Gemini 3, the four of us, John, Wally, Tom, and myself, moved into the astronaut quarters in the Manned Spacecraft Operations Building on Merritt Island, adjacent to the Cape Kennedy facilities, on March 15, 1965, a little earlier than I'd originally figured. But the folks at NASA wanted to give us plenty of time to acquaint ourselves fully with the Pad 19 launch complex.

These quarters are quiet, comfortably furnished, and you might think you were in some brand new motel. During the week before the flight all of us tried to get as much exercise as possible in the building's gymnasium, which is Tom Stafford's pride and joy, since he laid it out, complete with punching bags and one of those bikes you pedal like mad and get nowhere.

The night before the flight we had a quiet dinner with Al Shepard, Deke Slayton, Jim McDivitt, Ed White, and our good friend, Attorney Leo De Orsey, who has since died, and afterward we all sat around watching television. I can't remember what we saw, but I know we were all feeling pleasantly relaxed, and we headed for bed early.

At 4:40 AM, Tuesday morning, March 23, 1965, Deke Slayton woke us, right on schedule for our physical exams. These took only ten minutes; they were feeling us to see if we were still warm and breathing, I guess. Then back to one of steward Sam Piper's breakfasts. As we were only going to be in orbit for just over four hours, we didn't have to worry about a low-residue diet, so we had a whopper that included a two-pound porterhouse steak for each of us.

Certainly the atmosphere wasn't at all in the nature of "the condemned ate a hearty breakfast" sort of thing: Far from it. A lot of people who'd been in on Gemini from the beginning were on hand to see their work of months and years come to fruition: people like "Buzz" Hello, Gemini projects manager for the Martin Company, and "Mr. Mac" McDonnell, builder of our spacecraft. Walter Williams, who'd directed all of the Mercury launches, was there, as was Dr. Robert Gilruth, director of MSC, and Colonel Richard Dineen, Gemini program manager for the Air Force, and other NASA and industry officials. It was more like a Rotary get-together, and in the middle of it John Young was presented with a sixty-foot telegram signed by 2,400 residents of his boyhood home town, Orlando, wishing him a good trip. It seems that a wire service reporter had written a story to the effect that Or-

*Molly Brown's* crew, John Young in the lead, arrive at Pad 19 to begin the flight of Gemini 3. (W.B.E.S.S.)

lando had been taking the business of being an astronaut's home town pretty casually, and Orlando wasn't going to take that one lying down.

Mostly we talked about earlier space flights and about the terrific job the Ranger unmanned spacecraft was doing, sending back live television pictures until just before it crashed on the moon. The Ranger effort had done a lot, we agreed, to reassure people that we were still in there pitching in the Space Age, in spite of all the headlines given just a few days earlier to the achievement of Russian cosmonaut Alexei Leonov, leaving his spacecraft and floating in space at the end of his tether.

The two tiredest citizens at Cape Kennedy that morning were Wally Schirra and Tom Stafford. They'd spent most of the night checking out our spacecraft's systems.

Then it was time to leave our quarters for the drive to our Ready Room in the medical trailer, about a quarter of a mile from Pad 19. By now we all knew that the countdown was proceeding just about as perfectly as possible, and we were told that Christopher (inevitably "Chris") Kraft, Jr., our Gemini mission director, had said if things kept going as smoothly, "we'll be able to launch at 8:30 AM." We knew that if Chris Kraft felt that good, we had no reason to worry.

In the medical trailer, at Pad 16, the medics attached the sensors for heartbeat and pulse measurement, and slipped the ten-ounce amplifiers, which boost the strength of the medical electronic signals, into waist pockets in our "long john" undergarments, worn beneath the pressurized space suit. I saw that John Young, who isn't particularly fond of long underwear, had chopped the arms off his.

Then we suited up, helped by two old friends from Houston, suit technicians Joe Schmidt and Al Rochford.

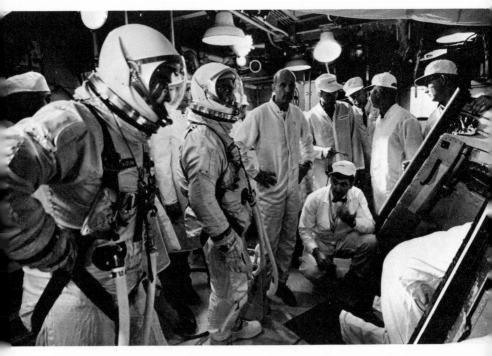

In the white room atop the erector tower, back-up pilot Tom Stafford looks on as crewmen prepare to assist Grissom and Young into the *Molly Brown*. (W.B.E.S.S.)

No movie queen ever got more attention. Deke Slayton consulted his watch and told us we were running a comfortable five minutes ahead of schedule, which is a nice feeling when your "launch window"—the optimum time for insertion into your planned orbit—is limited. As we finished suiting, Wally and Tom came in for a last-minute spacecraft briefing, and Wally described the sky outside as "fantastic." He was grinning from ear to ear, and so were we, because Wally had decided to dress for the occasion. He was garbed in the ruins of an old Mercury space suit, patched at the knees and out at the elbows, with bits and pieces missing here and there.

"I have suited up," he informed us solemnly, "just in case you two chicken out and turn the mission over to the back-up team."

Everything was still "green and go" when we left the medical trailer for the three-minute van ride to Pad 19 at 7:06 AM, via the "Barton FREEway."

The "Barton FREEway" was the mysterious creation of an Air Force warrant officer we knew only as "Gunner" Barton, a real old-timer who reminded us all of television's Sergeant Bilko. The original route from Pad 16 to Pad 19 had been long and roundabout, and pretty uncomfortable when we were all suited up for preflight spacecraft tests. We used to complain loudly that there ought to be a more direct toute. No funds, was the answer. Well, a few days before our launch, a straight-as-an-arrow road suddenly appeared between Pad 16 and Pad 19. The Gunner was looking especially innocent, so we knew he'd wangled it. But we weren't about to ask embarrassing questions.

Instead we painted signs in our quarters, saying "Barton FREEway," and sneaked out one night to post them along our new road. It became a part of astronaut lore, but

The erector tower is lowered as the countdown heads toward zero.
(W.B.E.S.S.)

the Gunner never did explain how he finagled the deal.

So, thanks to the Gunner, we were strapping ourselves into our couches aboard *Molly Brown* some six minutes after leaving Pad 16. The time was T minus 103 minutes, and by now we were five and a half minutes ahead of schedule as we began to make our final prelaunch systems checks.

By now Tom Stafford had gone to the Pad 19 blockhouse and Wally Schirra to Mission Control Center; Tom to act as communicator between *Molly Brown* and the blockhouse, Wally to serve as back-up for Gordon Cooper as Capcom (capsule communicator) after launch. With Wally was the Gemini 4 crew, Jim McDivitt and Ed White.

Everything was ticking along like a Swiss watch until T minus 38 minutes, when a leak was discovered in a pressurized liquid line running from one of our launch vehicle's propellant tanks. It took just one turn of a wrench on a valve to stop the leak, but the hold delayed the launch twenty-four minutes after our planned 9 AM lift-off.

With the leak repaired and the pad cleared of everybody, the big erector tower was slowly lowered, and we switched to our own internal power supply. This came from conventional batteries, since the fuel cells used in later Gemini flights were still under development. Now, we knew, the blockhouse doors were sealed. John and I went methodically on with our checks, the voices from the blockhouse keeping us abreast on the countdown.

"Open Stage One prevalves."

"Check Stage One prevalves open."

Our hypergolic fuels were about to meet and ignite.

"T minus zero! Stage One Ignition!"

There was a distant, muffled thunder ninety feet below our heavily insulated cabin. This was the split-second during which our Malfunction Detection System had to warn me if something had gone wrong, and I had both hands on the ejection ring between my knees, ready to yank it hard if the MDS indicators on our instrument panels indicated we were in trouble.

Three seconds later, lift-off! We were on our way.

"The clock has started," I told Gordon Cooper at the Control Center, as we roared upward and the sky began tilting slightly in our hatch windows. "There's roll program."

"Roger, roll," came back Gordo's calm voice. Then, a few moments later, as we entered the pitch program: "Roger, pitch. You're on your way, *Molly Brown*."

"Yeah, man," I radioed back to Gordo. I glanced over at John Young. He wasn't even holding onto his ejection ring. And we were, as John put it afterward, really hauling the mail. I shared his awareness of our tremendous speed, for after all, I'd gone only a third as fast on my Mercury flight.

I suppose I should have had some inspiring thoughts about being the first American to fly twice in space, but the truth was I was much too busy, as was John, and it wasn't until we reached orbit that we had a chance to talk about the incredible views flashing below our windows.

Test pilots are at home writing technical flight reports, but we don't do so good when it comes to rich, lyrical prose, which is probably why we haven't really come close to describing the incredibly beautiful views we've seen during our flights. For my money, there just aren't words enough to tell how it is to see a whole continent whirl silently by.

Even photographs can't do it justice.

The awesome thing is that you know that that tan carpet below you, looking so lovely and calm, is in reality the cruel Sahara and that that swirl of clouds, a beautiful, airy necklace, is in truth a fearsome hurricane, bringing death and destruction.

There is a clarity, a brilliance to space that simply doesn't exist on earth, even on a cloudless summer's day in the Rockies, and from nowhere else can you realize so fully the majesty of our earth and be so awed at the thought that it's only one of untold thousands of planets. The night sky is something else again, and in space the dawn really does seem to come up like thunder. Probably the most exciting view of all, though, according to the pilots of the rendezvous missions, is coming up on another man-made object, like the Agena Target Vehicle, sailing along in orbit.

One unexpected surprise I personally experienced—although why I should have been surprised beats me, considering all the maps I've studied—is that the continents look just as they do in the geography books. Maybe it's just that I never expected to be able to take in almost a whole continent at a time, and that's quite a thrill.

I've gone through the tape transcriptions of all the Gemini missions to see if I could find some quotable quotes about the scenery of space. The trouble is that most of the time the crews were simply too busy with the flight plan to wax poetic about the views, apart from the occasional "Man, oh man, this is really something," or simply "Great!" Which hardly gives you the idea. (In fact, Tom Stafford once wrote a newspaper scientific feature on space photography that ran close to seven hundred words without once mentioning the scenery. But get him talking on the subject and he's as enthusiastic as a Boy Scout after his first hike in the woods.)

So I guess you'll just have to take my word for it that the scenery of space is magnificent, and while I'm not given to sermonizing, all I can say is that if Major Gagarin found no evidence of God in space, he must never have looked out his cabin window.

There is a very special kind of space spectacular during re-entry, as we watch our jettisoned retro section begin to glow white hot as it burns up, and we are surrounded by almost every brilliant color of the rainbow as our heat shield ablates behind us. I can't think of any comparison on earth, not even this psychedelic lighting they're experimenting with these days.

Our launch sequence had gone perfectly, with booster and sustainer engine cut-outs (BECO and SECO) taking place precisely as scheduled. Shortly after lift-off, though, our on-board computer had told us we were going higher on the flight path than expected. Our booster was just a little bit "hot." Luckily, Gordon Cooper verified this from the ground, before we nosed down to get on the proper flight path. If we hadn't known what was coming, we could have been a little concerned.

But now we were in earth orbit, with an 87-mile perigee and a 125-mile apogee, just about as planned, and then, as we passed beyond the Canary Islands, all hell broke loose.

First, John told me that the pressure in the oxygen system, which kept us alive, had suddenly dropped both in our suits and in the spacecraft. Then I spotted some bad readings in other places. Reacting automatically, I yanked my vizor down and then it struck me: "If the oxygen pressure is really gone, it won't make any difference. You've had it already."

Actually, as it turned out, we had plenty of oxygen. We just didn't have the right readings. An electrical converter system which powered our instruments had malfunctioned.

John was smarter than I was. Figuring he wasn't suffocating yet, he reached up and switched on a back-up converter. We went right on breathing, with me feeling a little sheepish as I shoved my vizor back up on my helmet.

Now I had to do one of the limited number of planned scientific experiments. It was pathetically simple: All I had to do was turn a knob, which would actuate a mechanism, which would fertilize some sea urchin eggs to test the effects of weightlessness on living cells. Maybe, after our oxygen scare, I had too much adrenalin pumping, but I twisted that handle so hard I broke it off. (Later we learned that, by an odd coincidence, the ground controller who was duplicating our experiment, second for second, back on earth, had broken his handle in exactly the same fashion.)

About this time John was supposed to check out some of our space meals. The meals we had with us included some in plastic bags, into which we had to insert a water gun to reconstitute the dehydrated food inside. I was concentrating on our spacecraft's performance, when suddenly John asked me, "You care for a corned beef sandwich, skipper?"

If I could have fallen out of my couch, I would have. Sure enough, he was holding out an honest-to-john corned beef sandwich.

He'd known that I wasn't exactly wild for the meals

the nutritionists had dreamed up for us, so he'd had the sandwich made up at a Cocoa Beach restaurant and tucked it into one of the pockets of his space suit for my delectation. So I thanked John and took a bite, but crumbs of rye bread started floating around the cabin, and it became instantly obvious that our life-support system wasn't prepared to cope with the high-powered aroma of genuine kosher corned beef in the confined area of our cabin, so reluctantly, I stowed it away. After the flight our superiors at NASA let us know in no uncertain terms that non-man-rated corned beef sandwiches were *out* for future space missions. But John's deadpan offer of this strictly nonregulation goodie remains one of the highlights of our flight for me.

I'll admit, as test pilots, John and I weren't quite as fascinated with sea urchins and space food as we were by the chance to carry out some real space "firsts," changing our orbit and nudging our spacecraft from one flight path to another, or "changing plane." To accomplish these maneuvers, we used two types of thrusters. These were the big translation thrusters, which move the whole spacecraft from place to place. Smaller attitude thrusters control the spacecraft's position in whatever place it is—that is nose up or down, blunt end forward or back, nose turned right or left, and so on. You might compare the translation thrusters to the motor of a conventional airplane, and the attitude thrusters to the control surfaces, like the ailerons and rudder.

To our intense satisfaction we were able to carry out these maneuvers almost exactly as planned, confirming that our Gemini spacecraft was capable of rendezvous missions, in which changes of orbit and flight path are a requirement. To the best of our knowledge no astronaut or spacecraft had ever accomplished these maneuvers before.

The longer we flew, the more jubilant we felt. We had a really fine spacecraft, one we could be proud of in every respect.

Almost before we could believe it, it was time to prepare for the most critical part of our flight, retro-fire and reentry. This is when you know the whole world is watching you, holding its breath, and giving a sigh of relief along with you when those retro-rockets fire.

On Gemini 3 we had something else going for us. Thanks to our spacecraft's ability to maneuver, we had made a preretro-fire maneuver during our third orbit that lowered our perigee to only 52 statute miles, so we could have reentered even if our retro-rockets had failed, possibly an orbit later.

But they didn't fail, and what a sight that was. And what a comfortable feeling as our couches slammed our backs as each of the retro-rockets ignited and we began to sense the G-forces or reentry. Once again we became conscious of our tremendous speed as flames and frgaments from our ablating heat shield streaked past our windows.

Then our on-board computer told us we would land far short of our recovery carrier, the *Intrepid.* And here we were able to bring off another first, by performing two banking maneuvers during the reentry phase to give us maximum lift. This reduced the error considerably and allowed us to land only fifty-eight miles short of the predicted landing point. This controlled reentry technique was later so refined that the last two Gemini missions landed within sight of their recovery carrier.

The one real surprise to me was the jolt we both got when our main chute deployed. The harness is so rigged that the spacecraft is snapped from a vertical to a 45-degree landing attitude after the chute fills. It snapped, all right. John and I were both thrown against our windows, and I banged into a knob that punctured my face plate. John's face plate was scratched. And then we were in the water.

It was 2:15 PM. The flight of Gemini 3 had taken four hours and fifty-three minutes. John and I had been around the world three times.

Our splashdown point was only nine and one-half miles from the Coast Guard cutter *Diligence,* but by the time its helicopter was overhead, a pararescue team, dropped by an Air Rescue Service C-54, was in the water, and minutes later our flotation collar was being attached by another team dropped by a navy helicopter.

In all honesty I must state that my first thought as we hit the water was, "Oh my God, here we go again!"

The Gemini spacecraft is designed so that the left window, my window, will be above water after landing, but instead of looking up at blue sky, I was peering down at blue water. I realized that I still hadn't cut loose our parachute, and the wind was blowing it across the water, dragging us along underneath like a submarine. Remembering that prematurely blown hatch on my *Liberty Bell 7,* it took all the nerve I could muster to reach out and trigger the parachute-release mechanism. But with the parachute gone, we bobbed to the surface like a cork in the position we were supposed to take.

It was, to put it bluntly, hot as hell inside the spacecraft, and that, coupled with the pitching and rolling, gave both of us some uncomfortable minutes of seasickness. John managed to hang on to his meal, but I lost mine in short order. Then we climbed out of our space suits. From our pararescue team and our swimmers we learned that the *Intrepid* wouldn't arrive on the scene for about an hour and a half, so we decided to ask for a helicopter pick-up.

I left the spacecraft first because my hatch was the one fully out of the water and could be opened without danger of flooding the cabin. John Young told me that this was the first time he'd ever seen a captain leaving his ship first, so I promoted him to captain on the spot, which, he later claimed, entitled him, as a navy man, to rechristen our spacecraft the USS *Molly Brown*.

There were a couple of regulation Navy blue bathrobes waiting for us in the recovery helicopter, and these over our long johns must have given us the appearance of a couple of guys waking up after a big night at a convention when we landed on the *Intrepid*.

After a moving reception on the *Intrepid*'s vast flight deck, with crewmen perched everywhere, John and I moved below decks for our postflight physical examinations and debriefing sessions.

"Debriefing" is one of those service terms that give English professors the willies. What it really amounts to is a verbal account of the mission, which is taped for later study and comparison with the telemetered data, while the crew's memory is still fresh enough to encompass little details that might be overlooked or forgotten later. As they say in the detective novels, you're supposed to "spill your guts" to the debriefing interrogators, gripes and all. If John and I had any major gripes, I can't remember them. *Molly Brown* had done everything we'd asked of her, with a fast submarine ride thrown in for free.

With debriefing and physicals completed, we were flown back to a rousing reception and parade at Cape

Kennedy, which really flipped its collective lid at our safe return. My wife, Betty, and Barbara Young were there to meet us, and so were my folks and the senior Youngs, and that was a reunion none of us will ever forget.

After this John and I were heaved to the press. Well, we certainly weren't noted for being terribly gabby, but this time we sort of outdid ourselves answering questions, and soon John's dry wit had the reporters roaring with laughter. One of them finally asked if our flight had succeeded in making extroverts out of us.

To this John's solemn reply was, "I think Zero-G would make an extrovert out of anybody."

The following day, March 26, we were flown to Washington to meet President Johnson and receive from his hands the NASA Distinguished Service Medal and the citation that accompanied it. Both of us were delighted when the President awarded the same medal to Dr. Robert Seamans, director of the Gemini program for NASA. For me, personally, the finest reward I received was the opportunity for my wife and two sons to meet and shake hands with the President of the United States and Mrs. Johnson, and with Vice President Humphrey. It was, I know, a moment that Scott and Mark Grissom will remember for the rest of their lives.

Our visit to the White House was followed by a ticker-tape welcome to New York and other cities, where the enthusiasm was really tremendous to see. Looking back now, after so many more spectacular Gemini missions have been flown with much less public acclaim, I think I can understand the reason behind the gigantic outpouring of goodwill John and I received for our relatively easy flight. After all the Russian space spectaculars, the United States was back in the manned-space-flight business with probably the most sophisticated spacecraft in the world, or out of it. Our reception was the public's way of expressing pride in a national achievement.

But a Gemini mission didn't end with splashdown. Each was subject to an intensive postflight analysis, a kind of scientific post mortem. Our reentry "error," to give it its official name, which put us down fifty-eight miles from the *Intrepid*, was subjected to the most intensive scrutiny, and found to be the consequence of the fact wind-tunnel tests simply weren't capable of providing a truly definitive answer concerning the Gemini spacecraft's lifting capability. From the data compiled during our reentry, NASA scientists and engineers had a much better understanding of the spacecraft's true capability for maneuver, and this knowledge led to the near-pinpoint accuracy of later Gemini landings. Otherwise, *Molly Brown*'s was found to have been almost a pure "textbook" flight.

With the assurance they had a truly "spaceworthy" craft in Gemini, NASA planners knew they could go full steam ahead, and go they did. I doubt that any but a tiny minority of the press that covered our flight believed Gemini 4 would be ready for launch less than three months later, and I'd bet my bottom dollar that nobody at all expected Ed White to take his "walk in space" during that flight; or expected the last Gemini mission to be flown just under eighteen months later.

I do know if NASA had asked John and me to take *Molly Brown* back into space the day after splashdown, we would have done it with pleasure. She flew like a queen, did our unsinkable *Molly,* and we were absolutely confident that her sister craft would perform just as well. It didn't take long for us to be certain that our confidence wasn't misplaced.

# CHAPTER 12

# "It's Been Our Pleasure, Mr. President."

MINUTES AFTER John Young and I landed aboard the *Intrepid*, we received a telephone call from President Lyndon Baines Johnson in Washington. At a moment like that you are too excited about talking to the President to remember every word spoken. But, thanks to *The New York Times*, I've been able to see a transcript of our conversation, and the President said a lot of things John and I, and indeed all of us in the astronaut program, think should be said about our nation's space aims.

So I think that conversation deserves a place in this informal narrative.

THE PRESIDENT: Gus? This is Lyndon Johnson. How

are you? We have all been following every moment of your flight today since the lift-off this morning, and I wish I could have been there to meet you as I was when John Glenn took his.

I know both of you fellows are mighty happy and the entire nation is happy too. I know that I speak for the rest of this country when I tell you that we are very proud of you and that we are very grateful for your safe return.

Your mission, Gus, confirms once again the vital role that man has to play in space exploration, and particularly in the peaceful use of the frontier of space. I am sure you would be the first to say that on this flight, as well as on our other manned flights in space, there were heroes on the ground as well as in space, and the record made by men like Jim Webb, Dr. Dryden and Dr. Seamans,* as well as all of those at the cape, Cape Kennedy, and around the world, is a very proud record under Project Mercury and now on Project Gemini. And to all of those who have helped make our space flights safe and successful, I want to, through you and through others that are listening, say "well done."

I remember, Major, some very anxious moments you had and we all lived through with you on the *Liberty Bell,* and today apparently the *Molly Brown* was as unsinkable as her namesake and we are all mighty happy about it.

I know your work still goes on. As soon as you have completed your briefings there that you must go

---

* James E. Webb, Administrator of the National Aeronautics and Space Administration; Dr. Hugh L. Dryden, Deputy Administrator of NASA, since deceased; Dr. Robert Seamans, Gemini Program Director for NASA.

through, and get a little rest, I hope you will come to Washington on Friday if at all possible. We'll be looking forward to seeing you then, and we'll try to extend the welcome of all Americans to you.

Our prayers have been with you and are with you and your families. You have upheld a very fine tradition, and I want you to know again how proud we are of you, for your dedication, for your devotion.

America, as you know and as every citizen should know, has no purpose in space whatever except peace, and your personal contributions to this program will never be forgotten, and we shall continue on our steady course in our further explorations, and we will always remember this great day for you and John Young. After we get through talking, if I could I would like to say a word to John.

Now, you want to cut in, Gus?

GRISSOM: John is right here beside me. We had a very thrilling and wonderful flight today. I want you to speak with John.

YOUNG: Hello, Mr. President.

THE PRESIDENT: John, glad to hear you. How are you feeling?

YOUNG: Just fine, sir. It was a wonderful ride.

THE PRESIDENT: Well, I'm glad to have you back home.

YOUNG: Boy! Only thing wrong with it, it didn't last long enough.

THE PRESIDENT: Well, we'll try to work that out for you in the days ahead.

YOUNG: Yes, sir.

THE PRESIDENT: I'm looking forward to seeing you Friday. Can you make it?

YOUNG: Yes, sir, we'll be there.

THE PRESIDENT: Well, I salute both of you and all the folks that work with you, and please know you have the nation's gratitude and admiration.

YOUNG: It's been our pleasure, Mr. President.

THE PRESIDENT: Thank you, John. Goodbye, Gus. So long.

What made the President's remarks so important to me was his emphasis on the peaceable use of space.

Historically, every period of accelerated technological development has coincided with a war; it was our technology or theirs. It was a matter of survival, and out of the whole ugly mess came some undoubted advantages. But isn't this a terrible way to make progress?

To my knowledge no war in history has produced so much new scientific and technical knowledge as has the peaceful "race" to the moon. New metals, ceramics, and plastics by the score are now available to do even such mundane tasks as does my wife Betty's Pyroceran baking dish, which she can take out of the refrigerator and pop in the oven without a worry that it will break. And take miniaturization: I've heard a research scientist predict that it won't be long before we develop a minute type of radar, on the order of a bat's cry, that could allow a blind person to navigate by its beep. We've put up unmanned satellites to do jobs that were impossible less than ten years ago, like transoceanic television, for example. Satellites now make pinpoint ship navigation possible, and follow the world's weather.

The list of advances is nearly endless, and all of them have been made without a shot fired in anger. I'm sure it will keep right on growing as we move along into the Apollo program.

When I was a youngster back in Mitchell, Indiana, Dick Tracy's wrist radio was a far-out cartoonist's fantasy. Nowadays it's old hat.

Well, people ask me, wouldn't all these things have come along anyway, sooner or later? Perhaps so, but things don't usually get themselves developed until there's a need for them. If the ancient Phoenicians hadn't needed new markets, they probably wouldn't have got up the nerve to sail over the horizon to lay the foundations for the science of navigation. So far as I know, since St. Patrick the Irish have never invented a snake trap.

That there are military aspects to space is undeniable, and with his infinite capacity for making trouble for himself, man will probably find and make use of them. As spacecraft navigation and maneuver techniques are refined, we'll have the capability to inspect unidentified satellites and discover their functions. Our own Department of Defense would be derelict in its duty if it didn't monitor our own and foreign space programs closely.

But the basic intent of our United States space program is one of peaceful exploration, and so, God willing, it will remain. Like Antarctica, space should belong to nobody and to everybody.

CHAPTER 13

# Long-Duration Flights

WITH THE CONCLUSION of the developmental phase the Gemini program moved swiftly on to long-duration flight. Until the flight of Gemini 4, on June 3, 1965, the longest any American astronaut had been in space was the thirty-four-hour twenty-minute flight of Gordon Cooper in his *Faith* 7, in early May, 1963, which concluded the Mercury program.

The long-duration flights were intended to answer a lot of questions bearing directly on the Apollo moon mission, perhaps the most significant of which were medical. In a sense the crews who flew the Gemini 4, 5, and 7 long-duration missions were serving the rest of us as guinea pigs, actually risking their health and lives to discover

Atlas-Agena lift-off! The nose cone will be jettisoned in orbit to uncover the Agena's docking collar. (W.B.E.S.S.)

the human body's reaction to and tolerance of the space environment over prolonged periods.

Just to give you an idea, here are some of the pre-space-flight medical predictions about the consequences of weightlessness: anorexia, or lack of appetite; nausea, disorientation, sleepiness, sleeplessness, fatigue, restlessness, euphoria, hallucinations, diuresis, gastrointestinal disturbance, muscular incoordination, muscle atrophy, and urinary retention. If a man were to come back from a moon mission suffering from all the ailments I've just listed, he'd be a great candidate for the morgue.

NASA also wanted to find out how long the complex spacecraft systems it had developed would operate without serious malfunctions or unacceptable deterioration. Not even the severest acceptance test on earth can duplicate the ultimate test of the space environment.

Long-duration flights also provided time for the crews to perform a great many scientific experiments, not all of which were directly concerned with manned space flight, which could not be accomplished during the very busy schedules involved in rendezvous-and-docking flights.

I would like to emphasize that these long-duration flights were neither planned nor considered as endurance tests or space spectaculars. Any of the three would have been instantly terminated had serious problems developed.

On the strictly practical side the longer flights also constituted lessons in spacecraft housekeeping. If there was ever a need for a place for everything and everything in its place, it is in the cabin of a spacecraft. Otherwise you end up inside a flying wastebasket with the junk floating around in front of you.

To be honest I don't think NASA was ever really worried about the psychological aspect of two men being confined for as long as two weeks inside the the Gemini spacecraft, even though Dr. Charles A. Berry, the MSC's chief of Medical Programs, writing after Gemini 7, calls the absence of psychological difficulties "truly remarkable." For this a lot of the credit must go to the NASA people who selected the flight crews.

Gemini 4 was flown by the crew of Command Pilot James A. McDivitt and Pilot Edward H. White, II, the first crew selected from the second group chosen for astronaut training. Jim is a Chicagoan and graduated from the University of Michigan under Air Force auspices following combat flying in Korea. Ed White, whose father is a retired Air Force major general, was born in San Antonio, Texas, and graduated from the United States Military Academy, with later studies at the University of Michigan, where he first met Jim. Ed has two children, while Jim has three. And Ed claims to have the biggest astronaut appetite of all, and regards a porterhouse steak merely as openers.

Gemini 4 differed from the following long-duration flights in that its flight plan included EVA. This was pretty much a last minute decision. When the original flight plan was made Ed's EVA equipment, including the special EVA suit and the hand-held self-propulsion unit for maneuvering outside the spacecraft cabin, were still under development. It was only ten days before the Gemini 4 mission that NASA qualified the EVA gear for use in space.

Not surprisingly, it was Ed's spectacular accomplishment that got most of the headlines, for where the Soviet cosmonaut Alexei Leonov, the world's first man to leave his spacecraft, had simply tumbled at the end of his tether, Ed actually controlled his own movements and so proved that man could function meaningfully outside of the spacecraft environment. The long-range implication of this first controlled EVA was clear: Using much more sophisticated equipment, man will someday be able to assemble space stations in space, inspect or repair satellites, and of course, explore the moon on foot. Or, now that we have perfected our rendezvous technique, EVA will enable future astronauts to rescue crews from malfunctioning spacecraft.

(Jim and Ed were backed up by Astronauts Frank Borman and James A. Lovell, who were to fly the final and longest of the Gemini long-duration missions, Gemini 7, to its triumphant conclusion.)

Their primary objectives were to evaluate and demonstrate the spacecraft's performance during a four-day flight, and their own reactions to the space environment for so long a period. The secondary objectives included EVA, in- and out-of-plane maneuvers, and a step toward rendezvous, during which the crew would try to "station-keep" on the second stage of their Titan II launch vehicle. *Station-keeping* is a Navy term and means keeping a more or less fixed distance from a specified object, being "on station," like destroyers hovering near an aircraft carrier; close enough for the carrier's protection, far enough to avoid collision.

So on June 3, 1965, after an hour-and-sixteen-minute hold caused by difficulties in lowering the erector tower on Pad 19, Jim and Ed lifted off for a perfect launch at 10:16 AM, EST. My own slot during this flight was at MSC in the Mission Control Center, which was getting its first workout following its completion. I served as chief capcom, relaying information back and forth between the crew and Chris Kraft.

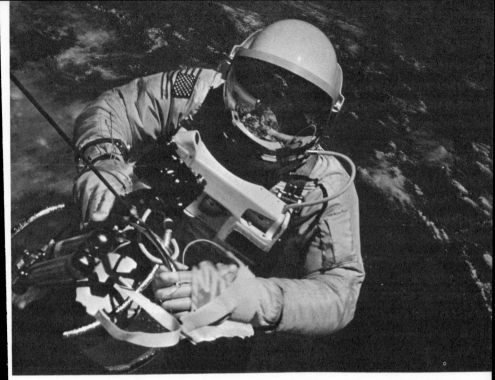

Using his hand-held maneuvering unit, Ed White leaves the Gemini 4 space-craft to become the first American to walk in space. (W.B.E.S.S.)

How Command Pilot Jim McDivitt saw his pilot making history.
(W.B.E.S.S.)

Eight minutes after lift-off Gemini 4 was in its 100-175 statute-mile orbit, precisely as planned, and the second stage of the launch vehicle was jettisoned, after which Jim turned the spacecraft blunt end forward, so the crew could observe the following chunk of the Titan. Unfortunately for everybody's hopes it was tumbling badly, and it soon became apparent that it was flying in another orbit. If that continued, the attempt to keep station on it would require an excessive amount of fuel. At Jim McDivitt's suggestion Chris Kraft agreed that the effort should be abandoned. But, as Jim later noted, the effort did point out that the orbital mechanics involved in a rendezvous were a little more involved than had been expected.

Ed White's EVA was scheduled for early in the flight—when he would be fresh and ready to encounter any difficulties—and it would take place for the most part over the United States and in daylight.

There was one tense moment when Ed's hatch was unlocked after the spacecraft cabin atmosphere had been reduced to a vacuum. The crew's space suits were bleeding just enough oxygen to create a small pressure which popped the hatch open, and Jim had to hang on for dear life to the lanyard mechanism controlling the hatch, to prevent it from flying open too suddenly and possibly causing such damage it couldn't be closed again.

With the hatch fully open, Ed stood up and began attaching a camera, which would record his movements, and over Hawaii, Chris Kraft gave him the word to begin EVA.

"What I tried to do was actually fly with the gun," Ed said later, speaking of his hand-held Astronaut Maneuvering Unit, or AMU, "and when I departed the spacecraft there was no push-off whatsoever. Seconds later I knew we had something with the gun, because it was actually providing the impulse for my maneuvers, giving me the opportunity to control myself where I wanted to go out there. And control was the big thing we were trying to demonstrate in our EVA operation.

" 'The maneuvering unit is good,' I told Houston. 'The only problem I have is that I haven't got enough fuel. I've exhausted the fuel now, and I was able to maneuver myself down to the bottom of the spacecraft, and I was right up on top of the adapter . . . I'm looking right down now, and it looks like we're coming up on the coast of California, and I'm going in slow rotation to the right. There is absolutely no disorientation association.' "

Ed's last statement was the one the space medics back at Houston were waiting to hear, but even Ed, I think, was surprised at how much of, and in what detail, he could see the earth.

"There was absolutely no sensation of falling," Ed told me after the flight, "and very little sensation of speed, other than the same kind of sensation we had in the spacecraft, very similar to flying over the earth at about 20,000 feet.

"The views continued to be spectacular. The one I remember best is as we came over Florida. Looking down, I could see all the lower part of the state, the island chain of Cuba and Puerto Rico. And that was about my last look, too, since that was when Chris Kraft gave me the word to come back in. I understand that during one of the medical press briefings there was some question about my staying out too long, as if I'd been hit by something like what sometimes hits deep-sea divers, the narcosis of the deep, or a kind of euphoria. Well, I can say in all sincerity and honesty that I enjoyed EVA very much, and I was sorry to see it draw to a close, and I was indeed reluctant to come in. But when the word came that the

EVA phase was over, I knew it was time to come in and I did. There was no euphoria, but getting back into the cabin took just as much time as getting out; I had to do the same things, only in reverse order, handing my gear in to Jim, and so on."

What the reporter who asked about Ed's "euphoria" overlooked was that Jim McDivitt was equally exposed to the space environment with the spacecraft hatch wide open, and Jim was controlling the spacecraft's attitudes against the various thrusts created by Ed's movements.

It was completely typical of Ed that he should have carried three mementoes with him during his EVA: a St. Christopher's medal, a gold cross, and a Star of David. As he put it, "I had great faith in myself and especially in Jim, and also I think I had a great faith in my God. So the reason I took those three symbols was that I think this was the most important thing I had going for me, and I felt that while I couldn't take one for every religion in the country, I could take the three I was most familiar with."

With Ed's EVA completed, the Gemini 4 crew settled down to a period of drifting flight, housekeeping, and experiments, and began learning a lesson applied to later flights, *i.e.*, that the alternating sleep-rest schedules, one man sleeping while the other kept an eye on the shop, was unsatisfactory. Their flight was to prove that the Gemini spacecraft was reliable enough to allow both crewmen to sleep at the same time, and this became standard procedure.

During the remaining days of the four-day flight, a curious Mercury myth was finally exploded. When he returned from his Mercury flight, Gordon Cooper was met with flat disbelief in some quarters when he described the details he had seen of the earth from his capsule including

"Come on back in." (W.B.E.S.S.)

ships' wakes, roads and railroads. "He's putting us on," was the usual reaction. No such thing, Jim McDivitt and Ed White reported; Gordo had been telling the truth all along.

For the Gemini 4 flight a computer malfunction made a computer-controlled reentry impossible, so the Mercury technique of a rolling reentry was employed, and the Orbital Attitude and Maneuver System's (OAMS) rockets were fired instead of the regular retrograde rockets as a checkout of their capability to serve as a back-up in the event of failure of the prime retrograde rockets.

So on June 7, after completing sixty-two-plus revolutions of the Earth in an elapsed time of ninety-seven hours and fifty-six minutes, Gemini 4 splashed down in the Atlantic, some fifty miles short of its recovery carrier the *Wasp*, at 12:12 PM, EST, with a helicopter pick-up half an hour later.

I think even the Gemini spacecraft's biggest boosters were pleasantly surprised by its superb performance, and as Dr. Charles A. Berry, our medical chief, noted, the flight succeeded in knocking down "an awful lot of straw men" from the medical point of view. The effort at station-keeping on their second stage, while not wholly successful, indicated that rendezvous was not an impossibility. And the way was wide open for Gemini 5, during which the first use would be made of the newly developed fuel cells, rather than conventional batteries, to develop electrical power for the spacecraft's systems.

One way to describe the operation of a fuel cell battery power system, to give it its full title, is to say that it *converts* energy, while a conventional battery simply *stores it*. It works something like this: The fuel cell converts the energy of the fuel, hydrogen, and an oxident,

The brains on the ground in the Gemini Mission Control Center near Houston. Dr. Robert Gilruth, Director of the Manned Spacecraft Center, standing, discusses a mission problem with Flight Director Chris Kraft; left, and George Low, MSC's deputy director. (NASA)

oxygen, to electricity by sustaining a continuous chemical reaction. It reverses the process of electrolysis: Instead of breaking water down into its components of hydrogen and oxygen, it *forms* water in a continuous controlled reaction that liberates energy in the form of electricity. This is used for on-board power. The heat created is rejected through the spacecraft's coolant system, and the water created is diverted into a bladder in the spacecraft's drinking water system, not to be drunk (although it could be), but to inflate the bladder and so provide pressure for the drinking water.

The main point is that for long-duration flight, the fuel cell's life is limited only by its supply of fuel and oxident, while a conventional battery will last only as long as its primary charge, unless there is a means of recharging available. Additionally, the fuel cell provides some saving in weight, which is always a prime consideration in spacecraft design.

Although long duration was the main objective, Gemini 5 was also intended to produce further information about rendezvous and the performance of the still-untested-in-space radar guidance and navigation system, which was designed to enable the spacecraft crew to measure the range, range rate, and bearing angle of another object in space from distances of up to 250 miles to near the docking phase. The spacecraft radar feeds its information into the on-board computer, which in turn feeds out data for the maneuvers necessary for rendezvous. To make this evaluation, Gemini 5 carried a Radar Evaluation Pod (REP) in its adapter section, for ejection during its first orbit. The REP was instrumented similarly to the Agena target vehicle, and contained a radio transponder for picking up and returning the spacecraft's radar signals. Battery powered, it was fitted with flashing lights for visual identification, and its life expectancy was planned at about six hours, or roughly four orbits.

By the time Gemini 5 was due for launch, the American public was considerably more sophisticated about space flight than it had been during the Mercury program, but there was still confusion concerning the terms *orbit* and *revolution,* and the seeming discrepancy between them. The two words aren't synonomous in the language of space. During our own space flights thus far, the spacecraft's course is measured in revolutions around the earth, so a revolution is earth-referenced, and one revolution is completed when the spacecraft passes over 80 degrees West longitude, which runs down from the North Pole through Pittsburgh, Pennsylvania, skirts the easternmost bulge of Florida, tips the westernmost bulge of South America and keeps on going to the South Pole. The time required for one revolution is about ninety-six minutes, give or take a few seconds.

Orbits, on the other hand, are space-referenced, and take about ninety minutes. Assuming you could take the earth away while the spacecraft was on an orbital course, the orbit would still take ninety minutes.

The longer time required to make a revolution is the result of the earth's rotation from west to east. As a spacecraft circles the earth, the earth itself moves about 22.5 degrees in the same direction. So, while the spacecraft completes an orbit in ninety-odd minutes, another six minutes are required for it to catch up with 80 degrees West longitude. If the spacecraft were launched to orbit counter to the earth's rotation, the time required for orbit would be the same, but the period of revolution would be shorter. United States spacecraft are launched eastward, in the direction of the earth's rotation, to take advantage of the speed thus gained, with the earth acting something like a slingshot.

The Gemini 5 crew assignments brought another Mercury veteran, Gordon Cooper, back to space as command pilot, with Pete Conrad as his pilot. Their back-up team was made up of two of the first civilian test pilots selected for Astronaut training; Neil A. Armstrong and Elliot See, Jr.

Gemini 5 lifted off at exactly 9 AM, EST, on August 21, 1965—after a two day delay caused by problems in loading the cryogenic, or very low temperature, fuels for the fuel cells, and bad weather—and promptly proceeded to turn into an extended cliff-hanger.

Some two hours into the mission, following the ejection of the REP and the beginning of the evaluation of the spacecraft's radar navigation system, the pressure in the oxygen tank feeding the fuel cells dropped from the desired level of between 800 and 900 pounds to about 70 pounds per square inch. To conserve power, the REP experiment was concluded well ahead of schedule, with the spacecraft now in a 216-106 statute mile orbit. Powered down, the oxygen tank pressure leveled off at 70 pounds per square inch and stayed there, while Flight Director Chris Kraft conferred hard with Elliot See, whose program specialty was the fuel cell. Chris had to make the terribly difficult decision whether to cancel the flight or allow it to continue, and ultimately determined to keep Gemini 5 in orbit, barring further problems. Even if the fuel cells had failed completely, back-up conventional batteries would have allowed the crew power for reentry and landing.

Communications between Gordo and Pete and ground

stations were kept to an absolute minimum, and Gemini 5 kept right on going, with its REP in sight for more than nine hours before it gradually fell away.

On advice from the flight director, Gordo had powered down an entire fuel section, something which had never been permitted during ground testing, but the remaining section continued to function to provide the minimum needed power for drifting flight. Gemini 5 was teaching everybody a lot of lessons in cryogenics and the operation of our new fuel cells.

With the REP experiment abandoned, Chris Kraft conjured up what became known as "The Phantom Agena," when on the third day of the mission it became clear that the fuel cell problem was clearing. To effect its rendezvous with its nonexistent target, the Gemini 5 spacecraft was put through four maneuvers during a period of two revolutions. They went off perfectly, and if Chris's phantom had been the real McCoy, Gordo and Pete would have beaten Wally Schirra and Tom Stafford to the punch by a few months.

The remainder of the Gemini 5 mission was taken up with experiments of one sort or another, and the usual problems of spacecraft housekeeping, following the pattern established by the Gemini 4 crew, with one pleasant addition; music "piped" up from MSC. Both men flew most of the mission with helmets and gloves removed, and they took their sleep periods together.

At eighty-four hours and forty-six minutes into the mission, Gordon Cooper reached, and seconds later passed, the individual space endurance record of 119 hours and six minutes, set by the Russian Cosmonaut Valery F. Bykovsky abroad his *Vostok V* spacecraft in June of 1963. Even when Pete Conrad and Gemini 5 passed Bykovsky's

Mission Operations Control Room, the heart of the global spacecraft tracking network. (NASA)

record, there was little or no fuss, either aboard the spacecraft or at MSC, just a lot of quiet pride.

Stowed aboard the spacecraft were a couple of dollar bills, which were a source of vast amusement to the crew.

"They were provided by the Fédération Aéronautique Internationale," Pete recalled later. "That's the organization that certifies all the world's flight records. The serial numbers of the bills were carefully recorded by the Fédération, and a representative was aboard our recovery carrier, the *Lake Champlain,* to retrieve them. Then he solemnly compared the bills with the serial numbers he had on record. If they agreed, the Fédération would, again with all due solemnity, certify that Gemini 5 had indeed surpassed the Russian record.

"What I can't for the life of me figure out is how you'd go about faking a space flight with the whole world watching, and I sometimes wonder what the consequences would have been if Gordo and I had substituted a couple of Confederate bucks for the others."

The last three days of the mission were spent in drifting flight with the spacecraft powered down. When, after the initial loss of fuel cell oxygen tank pressure, the crew had very cautiously powered up again, it appeared that over the entire period of the mission the system might produce an oversupply of water and another set of problems.

Gemini 5 splashed down in the Atlantic following retrofire near Hawaii during its 120th revolution, one orbit short of of the planned 122-orbit mission. The time was 7:56 AM, August 29, 1965. The touchdown was 103 statute miles from the *Lake Champlain,* due to an error fed from the ground into the on-board computer. Every space endurance record had been shattered, but no one

Gemini 6 begins its final approach to the world's first true rendezvous in space as it closes to within 80 feet of Gemini 7. (NASA)

doubted that the Gemini 5 record would not stand for long.

Postflight investigations showed the fuel-cell problem had been caused by the failure of a small electrical heating unit. The problem itself was less important, however, than the discovery that the complete electrical power system would operate far below what had been considered minimum conditions, and the fuel cells were, in fact, far better than anyone had dared to hope. Another barrier to long-duration space flight was down.

The rendezvous radar had functioned superbly. With the REP experiment aborted, the spacecraft's radar had, during an early pass over Cape Kennedy, locked onto a duplicate REP transponder mounted on a tower in the Merritt Island Launch Area (MILA), adjacent. The spacecraft radar measured the range to the tower to be 192 miles. Ground-based radars at MILA calculated the range from the tower to the spacecraft at 196 miles. As Chris Kraft declared, "You could take your choice as to which was correct."

So far as the physical condition of Gemini 5's crew was concerned, the medics jubilantly reported that Gordon and Pete were "healthy, happy, and aware."

The final and longest Gemini long-duration flight was that of Gemini 7, which last 330 hours and 35 minutes, encompassed 206 revolutions, and traveled 5,129,400 miles, between lift-off on December 4, 1965 and splashdown on December 18, 1965. To the best of my knowledge the records set by this mission still stand to the credit of Command Pilot Frank Borman and Pilot Jim Lovell and their back-up team, Ed White and Mike Collins.

And thanks to a set of circumstances, which in retrospect still seem beyond belief, the Gemini 7 spacecraft became the first target vehicle for the Gemini 6 rendezvous mission, which saw the United States with two space-craft and four crewmen in space at the same time, a feat never before or since achieved. But the rendezvous be-tween Gemini 6 and Gemini 7 has its proper place in the chapter devoted to this subject, which follows. Here, it seems to me, we ought to consider only the accomplish-ments of Gemini 7's fourteen-day flight.

It would be a mistake to think of Gemini 7 as simply an extended repeat of Gemini 5. Lift-off at 2:30:03 PM on December 4, 1965, was still another textbook operation, and once in orbit Frank and Jim began the most ambitious program of scientific experiments ever scheduled for a United States space flight, twenty in all. By this stage of the game, confidence in the integrity and performance of the Gemini spacecraft had helped Flight Director Chris Kraft decide to schedule the crew for simultaneous sleep periods and what amounts to our first "shirt-sleeve atmos-phere" flight periods, when first one and later both astro-nauts removed their space suits. These, incidentally, were a new design; much less weighty than the cumbersome suits John Young and I wore. They weighed only sixteen pounds on earth. Nonetheless, following the flight both Frank and Jim agreed that it was much more comfortable to doff them and fly in their long johns.

Most of the headlines on Gemini 7 were devoted to its dramatic role as the target vehicle for Gemini 6. The ten-sions and expectations of our first rendezvous in space tended to obscure the almost total lack of problems en-countered by Gemini 7. I suspect it was at about this point in time the public began to think of long space flights as routine. Neither Frank Borman nor Jim Lovell is given to needless chatter, and to the radio and television audience back on earth, they must have sounded as if space flight were as prosaic as a trip to the supermarket. With their flight, television and radio dropped the practice of second-by-second reporting of space missions, contenting themselves with an "all's well" report on regular news programs.

After the rendezvous with the Gemini 6 spacecraft on December 15, 1965, Gemini 7 carried on until its splashdown in the Atlantic Ocean on December 18, at 9:05:34 AM EST, just eight miles from the recovery carrier *Wasp*.

There was no longer any question: So far as man's adjustment to the space environment was concerned, so far as spacecraft systems could be depended upon to operate for extended periods in the space environment, man could aim with confidence toward at least a lunar-orbital flight. This would have been true even if the rendezvous had not been accomplished. But it was, as we'll see, so by the end of 1965, Gemini had, to all intents and purposes, accomplished all its major objectives, apart from actual docking.

If I've given the impression the astronaut's life during a long-duration flight is all play and no work, it's worth noting that both Frank Borman and Jim Lovell took along a favorite book. Frank chose Mark Twain's *Roughing It* (which seems appropriate), and Jim opted for one of James Fenimore Cooper's works. Neither of them finished their books. The twenty medical, technological, and engineering experiments they were scheduled to perform simply kept them too busy.

I haven't dealt at any great length with the various experiments carried out aboard the Gemini spacecraft because most of them were too technical to be of much interest to the layman, and they were, in some instances, only incidental to the flight. The results of these experiments are available, except where considerations of national security make it necessary to classify them, in the technical journals, and a lengthy description of them in this narrative would be out of place.

As 1965 ended, four more Gemini missions remained to be flown: The all important rendezvous-and-docking missions. But already the public was thinking ahead to Apollo. In one year Gemini had restored a shaky confidence and given it new strength, and now the question was no longer "If" but "When."

# CHAPTER 14

# Rendezvous-and-Docking Flights: Part One

IF NASA HAD had a Hollywood scenario writer, he could not have come up with a more dramatic introduction to the rendezvous-and-docking phase of the Gemini program than the flight of Gemini 6, with Wally Schirra as Command pilot, and Tom Stafford as pilot. John Young and I, as the back-up team, suffered all the agonies and savored the ultimate triumph, but I doubt if any one will ever really understand what Wally and Tom endured.

If all had gone according to plan, Gemini 6 would have lifted off on October 25, 1965, more than a month before the Gemini 7 flight. For the first time the United States space team was to attempt a dual count down of the Gemini-Titan II and its Atlas-Agena target, with the Agena

Rendezvous! How Gemini 7 looked to Astronauts Wally Schirra
and Tom Stafford 160 miles out in space. (NASA)

being launched from Pad 14, ninety-five minutes or one orbit, before the Gemini 6 spacecraft. Once in orbit, the Gemini would perform a catch-up maneuver to rendezvous and then dock with the Agena, repeating the docking operation several times.

Both countdowns went perfectly, and Wally and Tom were in their spacecraft, ready for the chase, when everything went to worms. The Agena simply vanished without a trace, probably somewhere in the Atlantic Ocean. Four more disappointed astronauts never lived, and the disappointment was the worse for our knowledge of the Atlas-Agena's fine record of previous performance.

For the time being Gemini 6 was scrubbed. In a purely negative way this was another space "first," but nobody was taking much pride in it. And until the engineers divined what had happened to the Atlas-Agena combination, nobody was inclined to launch another. But Gemini 7's flight was still scheduled, and there was Gemini 6, still ready to fly. Why not let the Gemini 7 spacecraft serve briefly as Gemini 6's target vehicle? Docking would have to wait, but the rendezvous might be achieved, and by now all concerned were sure it would be.

The decision was made.

Within twenty-four hours after the Gemini 7 launch, the Gemini 6 spacecraft and its Titan II launch vehicle were erected on Pad 19, ready for checkout tests following mechanical and electrical mating. Launch was set for December 12. The Air Force and NASA technical staff had accomplished the impossible, preparing Pad 19 for a second launch within eight days. The enthusiasm and know-how and just plain dogged work that went into the job was promptly recognized by the press and forthwith dubbed *The Spirit of '76*. A reporter friend advised me that the Cape Canaveral Press Club (they hadn't changed the name to match its assignment—Cape Kennedy) was split right down the middle between those who believed and those who didn't believe that Gemini 6 would lift off on schedule.

Lord only knows how many bets were lost on December 12, at 9:54:06 AM, EST.

At 9:54:07.5 AM, EST, Wally Schirra earned himself NASA's Distinguished Service Medal for his cool courage when the Titan II's Malfunction Detection System shut down its engines after ignition. Putting his faith in the MDS and his instruments, Wally made the command decision not to eject Tom Stafford and himself, with possible grave physical injuries to them both and a certain abort of the mission. Although the newspapers gave Wally and Tom full marks for not pushing the panic button, to this day I don't believe the public realizes that Wally and Tom were staking their lives on their knowledge of and belief in their Titan II launch vehicle. I doubt that the Martin Company will ever receive a finer tribute.

Immediate, intensive investigation discovered that the December 12 launch had been prevented by the premature dropping out of an electrical plug in the tail of the launch vehicle. But had the plug not done the job, a plastic dust-cover—used as a contamination preventative and inadvertantly left in place, obstructing the oxidizer inlet line of a gas generator—would.

At this stage of the game, *jinx* became one of the more overused words in the motel cocktail lounges of Cocoa Beach, along with the gloomy "Three times and you're out."

For all the records Gemini 7 was breaking and would go on to break, the Christmas season didn't appear to be giving Gemini 6 any presents. But nobody was giving up: Launch was rescheduled for December 15, with John Young and I making the spacecraft checkouts for the third time. Wally and Tom arrived some ninety-six minutes before lift-off. I'm afraid our grins were a little on the strained side because we had all had so much riding on this third try.

But this time everything clicked. Now all Wally and Tom had to do was find Gemini 7. Five houre and fifty minutes after leaving Cape Kennedy's Pad 19, they did just that.

It was a masterpiece of coordination between the Mission Control Center at Houston and the flight crew, involving a series of complex orbital maneuvers that had been previously "flown" only by computers. On the afternoon of December 15, the United States had two spacecraft and four astronauts aloft, maneuvering within a few feet of each other.

But even during this unparalleled feat the oh-so-human touch of Wally Schirra was felt. You'll remember that Schirra and Stafford in Gemini 6 were Annapolis graduates. So too was Jim Lovell of Gemini 6. But Frank Borman, in Gemini 6, was a lone West Pointer. Well, during one of his passes around Gemini 7 Annapolitans Schirra and Stafford felt their fellow grad needed some moral support in his confinement with one of the "others." He got it! There in Schirra's Gemini 6 window appeared a sign bearing the ageless legend "Beat Army."

Until this day a rendezvous in space had been roughly defined as one spacecraft's getting to within three miles of another. In Gemini 6 Wally and Tom were sometimes less than a foot away from Gemini 7. It had been previously agreed that there would be no physical contact between the two spacecraft, for there was still some uncertainty about the amount of static electricity that might exist on board, and of course there was no provision for docking. But so precise was the operation of the OAMS aboard Gemini 6 that Wally and Tom, following their mission, declared flatly that docking would present no problem.

The rendezvous, with both spacecraft flying in formation, continued for about four revolutions, following which Wally performed an orbital change to increase the distance between spacecraft to between twenty and forty miles. Aboard Gemini 7, although well aware they had just helped make space history, Borman and Lovell were again too busy with their experiments to pay much attention to their companions in space.

Page after page could be filled with technical language outlining the rendezvous technique, but the simplest way to describe it is as a chase in circles, with the spacecraft attempting to make the rendezvous gradually catching up with its target. The target, in this instance the Gemini 7 spacecraft, is maneuvered into a circular orbit. The chase craft is maneuvered to a lower circular orbit, hopefully in the same plane, but lower than its target, and so faster, thanks to the earth's gravitational pull. Thus it overtakes its target. As simple as this procedure sounds, it involves computations so complex and involved that only the advent of the modern computer made them feasible. Considering the vastness of space, the feat of Gemini 6 might aptly be compared with two fleas agreeing to meet at a certain speck of sand in the middle of the Sahara Desert —and doing it! It's small wonder Tom Stafford, who operated the Gemini 6 on-board computer as well as making his own computations and navigational plots, described himself as "busier than a one-armed paperhanger."

With rendezvous successfully demonstrated, Gemini 6 prepared for reentry, but not before its crew, remembering the season of the year and their four youngsters back in Houston, made an astonishing report to Mission Control Center. Of those who heard it, what one of us will ever forget the electrifying live report from space:

"This is Gemini 6. We have an object, looks like a satellite, going from north to south, up in a polar orbit. He's in a very low trajectory . . . looks like he may be going to reentry pretty soon. Stand by . . . it looks as if he's trying to signal us . . ."

In Mission Control, bewildered engineers first gaped and then broke into broad guffaws as they heard the sound of "Jingle Bells," played on a miniature harmonica, with real bells jingling. The irrepressible Wally Schirra had carried harmonica and bells aloft in a pocket of his space suit for just this occasion. It was no prank, Wally insisted afterward. "I think we convinced Chris (Kraft) that we did, in fact, have an unidentified flying object there. And I think the children of this country are happier that we might have seen something there."

Then, with Santa Claus's legend enhanced, Wally and Tom went on to add another first to their mission's splendid record by flying this country's first fully pilot-controlled reentry. They brought their Gemini 6 spacecraft down only thirteen statute miles from their recovery carrier, *Wasp*. And in the best Naval Academy tradition, Wally and Tom remained aboard until they were hoisted to the carrier's flight deck. My guess is that Wally was taking no chances his "Beat Army" sign might disappear.

With the dual missions of Gemini 6 and 7 completed and successful, 1965 ended a banner year for America's manned space program. We had put ten men and five

Astronauts Neil Armstrong and Dave Scott bring their Gemini 8
within two feet of the docking collar of their Agena target vehicle.
(NASA)

spacecraft into space and returned them safely, performed EVA, and achieved rendezvous. It was a pretty good record for a program that only two years before had appeared to be foundering.

By March, 1966, we were ready to go again with Gemini 8 and its crew, Neil Armstrong and Dave Scott, with their back-up team, Pete Conrad and Dick Gordon. This was to be a rendezvous-and-docking mission, with EVA scheduled for Pilot Scott. Rendezvous was planned to take place during the Gemini spacecraft's fourth orbit after a 1,050-mile catch-up. Dave Scott's EVA gear and the tasks he would attempt to perform were considerably more sophisticated than Ed White's on Gemini 4. Indeed, this was probably the most ambitious of the Gemini missions so far.

The mission began auspiciously at 10 AM, EST, March 26, 1966, with lift-off of the Atlas-Agena target vehicle, followed by the launch of Gemini 8 at 11:41:02, AM, EST, marking this country's first successful simultaneous countdown of two vehicles on the same day at the precise minute planned. At Gemini 8's launch the Agena target was in a near-perfect 161 nautical mile orbit, and during Gemini 8's first four revolutions, Neil and Dave were making the maneuvers for rendezvous.

The rendezvous went as planned and as the Gemini 6 crew had so firmly predicted, docking proved what Neil Armstrong called "a real smoothie." The electrostatic discharge between the two spacecraft, traveling at more than 25,000 feet per second, just never turned up, and the Gemini 6 spacecraft edged its nose into the docking collar of its Agena target as deftly as a commuter slips his car into his garage, with the crew keeping alert eyes on the Agena's illuminated instrument display. The next step was to check out the rigidity of the joined spacecraft, using the Agena's control system, by a 90-degree yaw maneuver. Again everything worked.

But then, some 27 minutes after docking, trouble!

The Gemini-Agena began encountering greater and greater yaw and roll rates; that is, it was spinning something like a barrel going over Niagara Falls, end over end. Our first thought was that something had gone wrong aboard the Agena, but swift checks told Neil and Dave it wasn't the Agena but their own Gemini spacecraft that was acting up. As matters grew rapidly worse there was reason to worry about joined spacecraft ripping apart from the strains imposed by the yaw and roll rates, with what possible consequences to the Gemini spacecraft's structural integrity no one could know. The Agena's control system was shut down, and the Gemini's was activated, but the situation remained unchanged. Clearly then, something would have to be done to separate, and using alternative Gemini procedures, the wild gyrations—the Gemini 8 was spinning 360 degrees a second—were reduced until the two craft could be safely undocked, with a minimum chance of recontact.

This was as close as United States astronauts came to a catastrophic situation during the whole of the Gemini program.

What had happened was the malfunction of a Gemini 8 yaw thruster, which continued to burn without command.

It says a lot for the coolness of Neil Armstrong and Dave that, even under the extraordinary circumstances in which they found themselves, they took the necessary steps, both to reset the Agena's command and communications system so its tape-recorded data could be telemetered back to Earth for analysis and to insure that the vehicle itself could be reactivated again as a potential future target.

In view of the yaw thruster failure, Houston, in the person of Flight Director John D. Hodge, decided to terminate the mission and bring Gemini 8 down in a planned secondary landing area in the western Pacific, some five hundred miles east of Okinawa and 630 miles south of Yokasuka, Japan, where weather conditions were reported favorable. This meant, of course, that Dave Scott's EVA was scratched.

Retro-rockets were fired over Africa, and splashdown took place at 10:22 PM, EST, March 17, 1966, with the crew picked up by the destroyer *Mason*. The reentry itself chalked up another Gemini 6 advance in the first use of an Auxiliary Tape Memory (ATM) for the on-board computer. Just prior to reentry this was substituted for the tape containing the program for rendezvous, with which Gemini 8 had launched, and it was the ATM that assisted Neil and Dave to their landing with astonishing exactitude. As Dave Scott put it, "It's pretty comforting to have a computer on board that tells you where you are, when all you can see out of your window for about thirty minutes is the Himalayas."

Despite its early termination the Gemini 8 mission provided a mass of valuable information, not the least important of which was the effectiveness of Department of Defense Recovery Force planning. An Air Force C-54 from Okinawa was over the splashdown point twenty-two minutes before Gemini 8 got its feet wet.

Then too, we had evidence that when our Gemini spacecraft's OAMS went sour, we could use, as Neil and Dave had done, the Reentry Control System as a back-up to

Docked! And the Agena's instrument display says All Systems Go.
(NASA)

stabilize the craft. The Agena had performed well, and even after Gemini 8 had undocked and reentered it was put through a demanding series of maneuvers, involving the restarting of its engines.

Gemini 8 flew only seven orbits, but it had succeeded in a rendezvous and docking with its target vehicle, and had undocked under emergency conditions, stabilized itself, and reentered exactly as planned, under the circumstances. (It must be understood here that NASA had planned, and trained for every contingency its collective minds could imagine.) Detection of the yaw thruster malfunction would insure improved controls on succeeding Gemini spacecraft to prevent a repetition. Gemini 8 did remind the public, briefly, that space flight was not yet as simple as a ride on a trolley car.

NASA announced Gemini 9 would fly on May 17, 1966. Elliot M. See, Jr., would be the command pilot; Charles A. Bassett, II, would occupy the right-hand seat, with Tom Stafford and Gene Cernan as their back-up team. After the announcement it seemed fate was throwing one rabbit punch after another at Gemini 9, which was planned as a rendezvous-and-docking mission, with EVA. The EVA gear provided for this flight was far more sophisticated than Ed White's little hand "gun," and was bulky enough that it had to be stowed in the spacecraft's adapter section.

Then, on February 28, 1966, tragedy: Elliot See and Charlie Bassett died instantly when their plane crashed as they came in for a routine landing at St. Louis for specialized mission training at the McDonnell plant.

Two more quiet, modest, and utterly competent men never lived. Shocked and saddened, Tom Stafford and Gene Cernan became the first back-up team to take over a mission for a United States manned flight. Jim Lovell and Ed Aldrin were selected as their back-ups. So Tom Stafford became the first astronaut to fly two Gemini missions. He would be followed by John Young, Pete Conrad, and Jim Lovell in Gemini 10, 11, and 12. (And at this stage of the game I knew there would be no more Gemini flights for me; now I was hoping for an Apollo flight.)

On May 17, Atlas-Agena lift-off took place at 10:15 AM, EST. Two minutes and ten seconds later it vanished.

When you have suited up, after all the preliminaries, and have made the final checkouts of your spacecraft; when you are waiting for that final word, "Ignition!" not all the words in the world can describe that solar-plexus punch, that total letdown when the mission is scrubbed. No bride left at the church could feel more miserable.

But NASA had a card up its sleeve called the Augmented Target Docking Adapter (ATDA), designed for just this contingency. This was a 2,400-pound device, constructed largely from off-the-shelf Gemini spacecraft hardware; 12 feet long and 5 feet in diameter, with instrumentation, lighting, and docking collar similar to the Agena's. Unlike the Agena, the ATDA had no propulsion system and could serve only as an inactive target.

On June 1, 1966, the Atlas-ATDA combination lifted off from Pad 14 at 10:00:04 AM, EST, with the Gemini launch set for ninety-eight minutes later. Thereupon the glitches, in the form of electronic difficulties in up-dating the on-board computer, got their licks in again, forcing postponement of the Gemini launch until June 3.

By this time some of the reporters were calling Tom Stafford *The Elevator Astronaut,* but Tom simply grinned and bore it with his usual good humor. Gemini 6 had flown after all its heartbreaks, and so would Gemini 9-A, as it was now designated.

On June 3, it did.

What followed was a classic rendezvous during the spacecraft's third orbit. And still another frustration. The conical shroud encasing the nose of the ATDA, and covering its docking collar and instrument display, had failed to release fully. The two halves of the cone were partly open and looked, Tom told Houston, "like an angry alligator out here rolling around."

Despite all efforts the shroud refused to budge, so plans for docking had to be scrapped. Nevertheless, Tom and Gene were able to carry on with two more rendezvous maneuvers involving different techniques, and crew activity was so strenuous and demanding that Tom requested Gene's EVA be postponed until the next day. The request was granted.

Initially Gene's EVA went exactly as planned, but there began to appear the first hints of trouble ahead and the possibility that the Gemini program's training for EVA was inadequate. Just about everything Gene attempted was considerably more difficult than he or anybody else had anticipated. Gene was working hard, putting a heavy strain on the life-support capabilities of his space suit, and as he moved aft to the adapter section, where he was scheduled to don the rather bulky Astronaut Maneuvering Unit (AMU), his vizor began to show signs of fogging, which swiftly grew worse. His efforts to rig the AMU added to the problems; its folding arms proved balky.

The fact was, Gene was in trouble, and when the fogging did not decrease during a rest period, he and Tom decided that further EVA was too risky to continue, especially when Gene's suit began warming abnormally. Houston concurred, the AMU experiment was scrubbed,

Tom Stafford's Angry Alligator grins evilly at the crew of Gemini 9 and refuses to shed its nose cone to uncover its docking collar. (NASA)

and Gene made his way into the spacecraft. The crew had been in extravehicular condition for two hours and five minutes.

Retro-fire came seventy-one hours forty-six minutes and forty-four seconds into the mission, and splashdown, less than an hour later in the Atlantic prime recovery zone, took place less than two miles from the carrier *Wasp,* in full view of television cameras. Tom carried on the Gemini 6 tradition established by Wally Schirra, and he and Gene rode their spacecraft to the carrier's deck for their heroes' welcome. This was controlled reentry with a vengeance.

Out of Gemini 9-A's flight came new and valuable knowledge of rendezvous techniques, and the growing realization that training for EVA would have to be improved further.

Three more Gemini missions were all that now remained to be flown.

CHAPTER 15

# Rendezvous-and-Docking Flights: Part Two

I DO NOT INTEND this book to be "the" official history of the Gemini program, for that task has already been accomplished in NASA's official records, and all the facts and figures are available for study by historians, scientists, engineers, and others caught up in the business of manned space flight. The scientist may find something of the greatest significance in a seemingly minor detail of a space flight which would have not the least interest for an engineer, while the engineer might see equal significance in a statistic that has no meaning for the scientist. For the layman such minor details, such statistics, have little relevance and even less interest.

What is important for him to understand is that by the

final three Gemini missions the United States manned
space flight program had advanced to such a stage that
these missions could be devoted to refinements of techniques already established.

To say this is by no conceivable means to diminish the
importance of these missions or belittle the problems faced
and solved by the crews who flew them. Indeed, the last
three Gemini missions were the most ambitiously planned
of all, and acquired experience and knowledge that will
be of benefit long after our first lunar landings. In these
missions we began mastering some of the problems that
will be involved in building space stations, for purposes
of earth observation or astronomy, or as launching plat-
forms for extended deep-space flights. And we were building a growing body of experienced astronauts with more
than one space flight on their records. As any fighter
squadron commander will tell you, the more veterans
you've got, the better the chances for the fledgelings when
they get to where the action is.

The final phase of the Gemini program got off to a
dazzling start on July 18, with the launch, in reverse order,
of Gemini 10 and its Agena target. My Gemini 3 pilot,
John Young, rode in the left hand seat as command pilot,
with Mike Collins as *his* pilot, and everything about the
launches went nominally (a word the general public was
now beginning to understand as meaning the space-flight
understatement for *flawless*), and a planned fourth revolution rendezvous was achieved, although with a somewhat larger fuel consumption than had been anticipated,
due to a "brute force" change-of-plane maneuver, which
cut down on some scheduled maneuvers.

Once successfully docked with their Agena, John and
Mike were ready to try something never before attempted

How the Gemini 11 crew of Astronauts Pete Conrad and Dick
Gordon saw the earth from 850 statute miles in space. Shown is
the northwest coast of Australia. (NASA)

in space, potentially hazardous, potentially promising. This was the restart of the Agena 10's primary propulsion system. A serious malfunction during this critical operation could blow both spacecraft to smithereens. In the docked configuration the Gemini's blunt end was forward with the crew facing aft, toward the Agena's rocket exhausts. They got a brilliant fireworks display as their target vehicle's engines restarted and sent them thundering out into an orbit with a perigee of 158.5 nautical miles and an apogee of 412.2 nautical miles, the highest altitude to which man had ever flown. Further maneuvers followed, to bring the docked spacecraft back down into a near-circular orbit, in preparation for still another rendezvous, about 207 nautical miles above earth.

This final Gemini 10 rendezvous would be with the Agena 8 target vehicle, still in orbit after its wild ride with Neil Armstrong and Dave Scott some four months earlier. When Gemini 10 finally undocked with its own Agena 10 target, the two spacecraft had been mated for forty-four hours and forty minutes.

There followed the rendezvous with the Agena 8 and the most extensive of the EVA planned for Mike Collins, who, using a hand-held maneuvering unit, approached the target and successfully retrieved a micrometeorite package intended to measure the size and impact of this space "dust." Earlier EVA, when Gemini 10 was mated with its Agena 10, had been curtailed when both Mike and John underwent a period of eye irritation that later cleared.

Reentry and recovery took place on July 21 without incident. The Agena 10, like the Agena 8, was left in orbit as a possible future target.

Gemini 10 achieved all its objectives apart from docking repetitions with its own target vehicle, which were precluded by the need to conserve Gemini fuel.

One of the things that struck me about this flight was that the breaking of the world's altitude record was purely incidental to the flight plan and occasioned little excitement, whereas when I was a high school boy, a new altitude record was a subject for headlines for days afterward. We were coming, I felt at the time, to regard the spectacular as commonplace.

Gemini 10's altitude record lasted less than two months, until the flight of Gemini 11 with its crew, Pete Conrad and Dick Gordon. This was another "third time lucky" mission. Gemini 11 was originally set to launch on September 9, 1966, but again a series of technical hitches combined to make a series of postponements that kept it grounded until September 12, and kept the back-up crew, Neil Armstrong and Bill Anders, as busy as beavers. But September 12 saw both the Agena and Gemini launched and effecting their rendezvous during the first orbit, right on schedule, with practice in undocking and redocking following for both crew members. One day into the mission Dick Gordon began his first period of EVA, using an umbilical, but no maneuvering unit, to get from the spacecraft to the Agena, to which he attached a tether intended for use later in the mission. As had been the case with Gene Cernan and Mike Collins, Dick Gordon found himself working a lot harder than his training had led him to expect, and simply keeping himself in position made the job of attaching the tether a long and difficult operation, although in simulations the attachments had been made in a matter of seconds. Fatigued and with his vision hampered by perspiration, Gordon, with Conrad's concurrence, decided to terminate this EVA period early and return to the spacecraft cabin for some much needed rest.

The following day the Gemini 11 crew restarted their Agena's propulsion to place the docked combination in a 741.5-156.3 nautical mile orbit, thus shattering the Gemini 10 record, again as an incidental to the flight plan and not as a primary objective. The high-orbit period was largely devoted to photographic experiments, and with these completed, the Gemini-Agena combination returned to a near-circular orbit of 164-156 nautical miles in preparation for operations, following undocking, with the tether Dick Gordon had attached earlier. The object of this exercise was to establish the feasibility of unattended station-keeping, using the principle of gravity gradient stabilization to save maneuvering fuel. This principle had already been demonstrated successfully in some of our unmanned satellites, and it deserves a word of explanation here.

Orbital space flight is really a continuous free fall, with the spacecraft attracted back to earth by the earth's gravity, except that as fast as it falls back toward the earth's center, the rotating earth drops away from under it so that it can't catch up. The closer the spacecraft is to the earth, the greater the pull of gravity, and so the faster it wants to fall. The further the spacecraft is from the earth, the less the pull of gravity, so its fall rate is slower. Thus if you could connect two spacecraft, one higher than the other, the higher, slower-moving space-craft would act as a brake on the lower, and the two would become a stable unit with their axis pointed at the earth's center of gravity, like a kind of giant dumbbell in space. In manned space flight this will allow a crew to tether onto, say a space station component, and then have a good night's sleep, confident that the other end of their dumbbell will neither come crashing into them nor go floating away, to be retrieved only by the use of valuable fuel, or possibly lost entirely. This is what Pete and Dick were going to check out during their tethered operation.

They were also going to try to rotate their space dumbbell, much as the earth rotates, with the middle point of the tether assuming the role of the earth's center of gravity, and in this fashion create a very small artificial gravity field of their own. The significance of this experiment was that if being weightless over very long periods, far longer than 14 days, should prove to be a physical hazard, provision of an artificial field of gravity might solve the problem.

Both experiments were successful, and following a rerendezvous with their Agena target, after the tether had been jettisoned, Pete and Dick came back in for the Gemini program's first fully automatic computer-plotted-and-commanded reentry, which splashed them down after seventy-one hours and just over seventeen minutes of flight, into the Atlantic under two miles from their prime recovery ship, the *Guam*.

During the tether experiments Dick Gordon had performed a second period of EVA, standing in the hatch without actually leaving the spacecraft cabin, which gave Gemini 11 the record for the greatest total time engaged in EVA, 161 minutes.

The success of Gemini 11 was followed and matched

just one month later by the flight of Gemini 12, with Jim
Lovell, command pilot, and Buzz Aldrin, pilot. Gemini 12
followed a nearly similar flight to that of Gemini 11, except for a high orbit, and showed the outstanding improvement in EVA underwater training by Buzz Aldrin's performance. The final Gemini mission, our sisteenth manned
space flight, was a nearly perfect operation which provided a triumphant conclusion to this country's second
manned space program. With its splashdown the United
States held every known space flight record.

The dual launch of the Atlas-Agena target vehicle and
the Gemini-Titan II took place on November 11, 1966,
the first space launch on a national holiday, Veteran's
Day. The third-revolution rendezvous was achieved as
planned, despite a failure in the Gemini spacecraft's radar
during the later phase, requiring a visual acquisition of
the Agena by the crew. Plans to ignite the Agena's primary propulsion system (PPS) were canceled when flight
controllers at Houston found aberrations in the system,
and docked-configuration maneuvers were performed
using only the Agena's secondary propulsion system. I've
said Gemini 12 made a nearly perfect flight: All its primary objectives were accomplished, but it was beset
throughout by a number of operational problems, like the
Agena's PPS. That Jim Lovell and Buzz Aldrin and the
crew at MSC were able to overcome them through the use
of alternative techniques and back-up systems demonstrates, I think, just how much space know-how we had
acquired from the previous flights.

The EVA on this flight, three periods in all, went off
far better than anybody had dared to hope; proof that
the underwater training was a valuable tool. Unlike his
predecessors, Buzz also had advantage of improved hand-

holds and footholds, along with a personal restraint tether to help him maintain his position with reference to the Agena and back in the Gemini 12 adapter section.

For the second time gravity-gradient stabilization was achieved, with the Gemini tethered to the Agena.

As the mission drew toward its close, difficulties were encountered with two yaw thrusters and the fuel cells, but retro-fire and reentry, using the same technique employed during the Gemini 11 mission, were exactly as planned, with splashdown coming at 2:21:04 PM, EST, November 15, 1966, within sight of the recovery carrier *Wasp*.

It was a magnificent conclusion to Project Gemini.

If, back in Houston, there was a little sadness that the program was finally completed, it was quickly dissipated when the press reversed roles and played host to the NASA officials charged with the postrecovery news conference, held at a hotel adjacent to MSC. The reporters, many of whom had covered every manned space flight since Mercury's inception, came thundering through with champagne for everybody! That was probably the cheeriest news conference in the history of manned space flight.

The awards ceremony that followed the Gemini 12 splashdown on November 23, 1966, was the opportunity for NASA to recognize and honor both Jim Lovell and Buzz Aldrin, along with scores of other individuals who had made truly significant contributions to the Gemini program's splendid success and many of whose names were almost completely unknown to the public. Theirs was a richly merited recognition.

So, in the years between Alan Shepard's flight in his *Freedom 7* Mercury capsule on May 5, 1961, and the conclusion of the Gemini program, the United States had logged 1,993 hours 39 minutes and 35 seconds in manned space flight. The 5,716,900-mile flight of Gemini 7 was the longest ever flown by man. The 850 statute mile altitude reached by Gemini 11 was the highest ever reached by man. The total of twelve hours thirty-one minutes of EVA was unmatched. We had achieved and mastered rendezvous and docking, along with the tethered, gravity-gradient-stabilized flight of two spacecraft.

We had performed dozens of scientific experiments never before possible, including some of the most spectacular and revealing photography ever made, of special value to geographers and geologists.

Yet all the records I've just quoted probably will fall within the next several years, when the Apollo programs get fully underway. Hopefully I'll help break one or two myself, for as I write these words I have been notified of my selection to be a part of the first Apollo crew, along with my good friends Ed White and Roger Chaffee. In most respects our flight will be a duplicate of Gemini 3, in that Ed, Roger, and I will be primarily concerned with checking out the spacecraft's systems and seeing whether it is both flyable and livable.

There is one aspect of the Gemini program I doubt its planners ever seriously considered, and this was the post-flight role of astronauts as ambassadors of goodwill. Nearly all the Gemini astronauts have been dispatched overseas, following their flights, to help explain America's space programs to our friends abroad, and this was a wonderful experience for all of us. It also gave some of us a chance to meet our Russian counterparts in space, including Yuri Gagarin, Pavel Belyayev, and Alexei Leonov, the first man to "walk" in space outside his spacecraft. These meetings were always friendly, and during a visit to the sixteenth

International Astronautical Congress, held in Athens, Gordon Cooper and Pavel Belyayev traded the wristwatches they'd worn on their space missions. What impressed all of us, I think, was the appreciation of foreigners for the openness of our space flights, and our willingness to admit failure or lack of total success, as when the flight of Gemini 8 terminated prematurely. Over and above the privilege of meeting distinguished people, there was the pleasure of travel for ourselves and our families—although this may sound a little odd, coming from astronauts. But orbiting in a spacecraft doesn't give you much chance to get to know the countryside.

Today, the Gemini program is history. We know it was a fantastic, almost incredible success. It accomplished every one of its major objectives by the time Gemini 12 splashed down in the Atlantic in November, 1966. Looking back, it seems unbelievable that only a few years ago Gemini looked about to fall flat on its face. Now the next step is the moon.

# CHAPTER 16

## Son of Gemini

As only Project Mercury could have made Project Gemini possible, so without Gemini we would not now be aiming for the moon with Project Apollo.

Why go to the moon in the first place?

That question gets itself asked a lot these days, and not only by the fundamentalists who argue that if God had wanted us to fly, He'd have given us wings. Some very eminent scientists have declared the whole project is pointless. Others have said if we insist on knowing what is on the moon, instruments could do the job as well. Why risk men's lives? Why spend all that money to visit a dead satellite with a wildly hostile environment?

My own answer, a purely personal one, goes something

like this: Suppose we reach the moon; then suppose the first moon explorers come back with a brand new mineral, one that doesn't exist on earth. Suppose that new mineral turns out to be capable of curing cancer, or restoring sight to the blind. In my book such a discovery would more than justify the whole project. Meantime, we're making all the technological advances I've mentioned earlier, and new ones are bound to come to light.

Why men instead of instruments and gadgetry? Well, consider our highly sophisticated and costly Surveyor lunar vehicle: As good as it proved to be, it could only secure a limited amount of information. To build a spacecraft capable of doing only a part of all a man can do would require something as big as a computer center.

Once we have established our capacity to put a spacecraft on the moon, as we have now done, I don't think human nature will be content to use machines instead of man himself. Our God-given curiosity will force us to go there ourselves, because in the final analysis, only man can fully evaluate the moon in terms understandable by his fellow man.

Another curve ball that frequently whistles past my ears is the one that says our space programs are taking up too much scientific and engineering talent that could be better used for more immediate earthbound problems. Actually, I understand that the *whole* NASA space program, manned and unmanned, uses only 6 per cent of the total national manpower pool of scientists, engineers, and technicians through its contracts with private industry. My personal hope is that as our space program continues, we'll need more and more of these people. Why? Because it can't help but make us a smarter nation in the long run.

When I was studying at Purdue, we learned our thermodynamics from an antique steam engine. When I went back in 1964, I found the engineering laboratories packed with the most modern equipment for the study of thermodynamics, some of which had been built by the students themselves. The young fellow who graduates from Purdue's Engineering School this year is going to know a lot more about thermodynamics than I knew, or know.

The same thing holds true for all the other sciences and technologies. We're turning out smarter, better trained graduates, and of them, as they say, we can't have too many. It used to be that a so-so engineer could always be pretty certain of getting a job, maybe designing cotter pins. Not any more. Today he's *got* to be good to get any kind of a job.

Only recently I was stopped cold by an advertisement published by North American Aviation, Inc., in a national news magazine. Its headline asked: "What Does It Take to Hand-Carry the American Flag to the Moon?"

Below this, in small type, were fifteen lines listing the scores of items and facilities required to do the job, from cameras, batteries, and wind tunnels to gyroscopes, telemetry, and computerized flight plans. Then, in large type: "And Three Astronauts, Seven-and-a-half Million Pounds of Thrust, 192,313,000 Americans and the Apollo spacecraft built for NASA by North American Aviation."

I blinked at the figure 192,313,000 Americans, and then realized that it was entirely accurate. All of us are involved in one way or another, even if it amounts to nothing more technical than paying taxes. I am not an economist, but I can't help feeling that Apollo and space programs to follow have created and will go right on creating thousands of new jobs and industries to meet needs whose existence we don't even suspect today.

So although this book was intended as an informal history of the Gemini program, since the Gemini program supplied so many of the answers to the Apollo program, it seems only logical that I should conclude with a brief look at our reach for the moon. This, after all, is what Gemini was all about.

The first thing that bowls you over about the Apollo program is the sheer thundering size of the operation. It is almost as if somebody had said, "Let's build New York City overnight." In fact, I'm not sure anybody who hasn't visited the Merritt Island Launch Area can really begin to appreciate the enormity of this project.

MILA is designed to be a true moon port, and by comparison, our Gemini Launch Complex 19 will look like something out of Li'l Abner's Dogpatch. I don't awe easily, but MILA awes the daylights out of me.

To begin with, its 87,000-acre site is nearly six times as big as the 15,000-acre Manhattan-sized Cape Kennedy Missile Test Center. As I write this, the heart of MILA will be Launch Complex 39, the pad from which the Apollo lunar mission will blast off.

Supporting this heart will be a flight control center, and adjacent to it, the enormous Vertical Assembly Building, or VAB, fifty-two stories high and encompassing more space than the Pentagon, capable of housing four Saturn V launch vehicles at once. From the VAB the Saturns will be moved to the pad, a mile or so away, aboard huge, self-propelled crawlers over a specially built eight-lane crawlway. The crawlers each carry their own 450-foot-high umbilical tower and the whole effect is something like a skyscraper on the move.

The object of the exercise, the reason behind all this vastness, is to land a Lunar Excursion Module (LEM) on the moon, allow its two astronaut occupants to explore for as long as four days, and then return them to safety.

The Apollo spacecraft will consist of a command module, a service module, and the LEM. The command module, which will become the reentry vehicle on the return to earth weighs something more than 8,500 pounds, at least 1,500 pounds more than the Gemini spacecraft. The service module, roughly comparable to the Gemini adapter section, weighs in at approximately 55,000 pounds, and the LEM adds another 24,000 pounds to the load the Saturn V launch vehicle must lift off the ground. The whole combination adds up to some forty-five tons, but this is for the lunar flight. For earth-orbital flights, the Saturn V will be able to put a 120-ton payload into orbit, a craft big enough to accommodate a small Rotary Club meeting.

The Saturn V will be this country's biggest rocket ever, generating about 7,500,000 pounds of thrust at sea level during the first-stage burn; 1,000,000 pounds of thrust at altitude during second-stage burning; and 200,000 pounds during the third-stage burn in space. Its maximum diameter, excluding fins, will be 33 feet, more than three times that of our Gemini-Titan II launch vehicle, and the overall height, with the Apollo spacecraft mated, will be 364 feet; roughly the height of a 36-story building. The fuel of the second and third stages will be liquid oxygen and liquid hydrogen, both explosive, and for this reason the launch-abort system will revert to the Mercury escape-tower design. Put together, the spacecraft and launch vehicle will weigh about six million two hundred thousand pounds, which comes out to at least three thousand tons, if my arithmetic is sound. That's about the tonnage of a respectable destroyer, John Young tells me.

Apollo-Saturn V on crawler emerging from the Vertical Assembly
Building at the Merritt Island Launch Area. (NASA)

In this titanic hardware, by 1970 three astronauts will lift off from Launch Complex 39 at MILA. The five-engine first stage will heave the monster off the ground at near-orbital speed and to near-orbital altitude before separation. At this point, the escape tower will be jettisoned. An abort after this would mean a normal re-entry procedure. The second stage will take it to orbit altitude, and then separate, with the third stage firing briefly to adjust the earth orbit. If all goes well, the third stage will be restarted to speed the spacecraft to escape velocity, some 25,000 miles an hour on an earth-moon trajectory for the 70-hour journey, and this achieved, the third stage will be jettisoned. After third-stage separation the crew will separate the command-service module from the LEM and reverse 180° to dock nose to nose with the LEM. Once this has been accomplished, the first of what may turn out to be several midcourse corrections is undertaken to put the Apollo-LEM combination into position to enter a precise lunar orbit. Once in this orbit, two astronauts will transfer from the command module to the LEM through the nose-to-nose hatch connection, and the LEM will be separated for its descent to the moon surface, leaving the third crewman in the command module.

The LEM will then lower itself to the moon surface by a combination of crew and automatic control, taking advantage of the moon's very low gravity to achieve landing with a minimum use of fuel. If things look dim, the LEM crew may elect not to land but to return immediately to the command module: Otherwise, they will land, and before doing anything else, make all the checks and preparations necessary for relaunch.

Then they will leave the LEM for their scheduled explorations and experiments, using entirely self-supporting space suits. Some of the two hundred pounds of experimental gear will be left behind to continue transmitting data back to earth when, after four days at the most, the astronauts relaunch to rejoin the command module in its lunar orbit. After docking, the LEM crew will reenter the command module, and the LEM will then be undocked to remain indefinitely in lunar orbit.

The flight back to earth orbit and reentry, at a speed higher than any we have so far experienced, will involve a still-untried technique, roughly comparable to skipping a stone across a pond. Using the Apollo spacecraft's lifting capability, the crew will initiate reentry by dipping first into the earth's thinner upper atmosphere to reduce its speed to an acceptable rate, and when this has been achieved, it will be flown down through the increasingly heavier atmosphere to its landing. The initial dip will have to be very precisely calculated, for with its retro-rockets fired, and no further means of reentry available, an error could send the spacecraft up and out of the earth's atmosphere into indefinite orbit with no hope for the crew's survival. Wally Schirra's word for the Apollo reentry maneuvers is, simply, "hairy."

But none of us has any doubts that it can and will be accomplished.

And beyond Apollo? Tentatively, the Apollo-applications program, which is still in the planning stages and will probably see the big Apollo spacecraft employed in earth orbital missions as a kind of flying laboratory/observatory.

Beyond that?

Just recenty I read a paper presented to a meeting of the American Institute of Aeronautics and Astronautics by Franklin P. Dixon, manager of Advanced Space Systems, Aeronautic Division of the Philco Corporation. It was entitled, "An Early Manned Mars Landing Mission Using the Mars Excursion Module." It made fascinating reading. Mr. Dixon's proposed Mars mission would last between 390 and 440 days, and land an MEM with a minimum two-man crew on Mars itself for a stay of between ten and forty days. As many as six astronauts might make up the crew.

In his conclusion Mr. Dixon writes: "The MEM development appears to be a logical extrapolation of our present technological capabilities into the not too distant future. Some engineering and fundamental research is still required to achieve this future capability and a reasonable development program of nine years is required along with the technology advances. Also, such a mission depends on other elements in our space program.

"It would not seem unrealistic to propose that a total manned Mars mission would require 10 to 14 years for successful accomplishment. . . . A manned trip to Mars could yet be a dream realized in our lifetime."

If I had read that statement as a high school boy in Mitchell, Indiana, it could only have been published in a science fiction magazine, and MEM would have meant a mean-eyed monster. Today it is a serious proposal presented to a distinguished forum of this country's top space scientists and engineers. That's how far we've come.

That's why this space business is so tremendously exciting, because it has no horizons. That's why all of us who flew in the Gemini program feel so lucky to have been in on the ground floor, so to speak, and no pun intended. Sure it would be wonderful to be the first man on Mars, but by the time he gets there we'll all be astronautical graybeards. Still and all, we'll have the satisfaction

Apollo-Saturn V on the MILA launching pad. (W.B.E.S.S.)

of knowing that he wouldn't be there if there had been no Gemini.

There will be risks, as there are in any experimental program, and sooner or later, inevitably, we're going to run head-on into the law of averages and lose somebody. I hope this never happens, and with NASA's abiding insistence on safety, perhaps it never will, but if it does I hope the American people won't feel it's too high a price to pay for our space program. None of us was ordered into manned space flight. We flew with the knowledge that if something really went wrong up there, there wasn't the slightest hope of rescue.

We could do it because we had complete confidence in the scientists and engineers who designed and built our spacecraft and operated our Mission Control Center and tracking network. It was they who made Gemini the success it was, and I'm proud and happy that we who flew the Gemini missions didn't let them down.

Now for the moon.

Seabrook, Texas
January, 1967

# Epilogue

WITHIN WEEKS after completing the first draft manuscript of this book, Lieutenant Colonel Virgil Ivan Grissom was dead, killed with his colleagues, Lieutenant Colonel Edward M. White, II, and Lieutenant Commander Roger B. Chaffee, in a flash fire aboard the Apollo spacecraft they were scheduled to take aloft on its first manned flight on February 21, 1967. Ironically, they died "on the pad" at Cape Kennedy, where they were conducting a full-scale simulation of their forthcoming mission.

It was this editor's high privilege to work closely with Gus Grissom in gathering materials for the book and suggesting its general organization, and as we worked together, to call him a friend. Quiet, modest, with a wry

Astronauts John Glenn and Gordon Cooper march beside the caisson bearing Lieutenant Colonel Virgil Ivan Grissom to his grave in Arlington National Cemetery. Elsewhere, other brave men, too, wept. (W.B.E.S.S.)

sense of humor never far below his no-nonsense surface, he had the rare ability to communicate complicated technological information in layman's language. He was, indeed, as many of the obituaries published after his death described him, "an astronaut's astronaut," giving his complete attention to the business at hand. Yet to watch him in his home with his wife, Betty, and his two sons, Scott and Mark, was to see space forgotten for the Little League standings. He was quick to give credit to his fellow astronauts for their accomplishments, and used to emphasize that it was the people on the ground who really made space flight possible.

For all his seemingly brusque exterior he was unfailingly considerate in his dealings with me. But my sense of personal loss is as nothing to the nation's very real loss of a skilled, utterly dedicated astronaut, the first man in the world to fly twice in space.

Tragic as his death was, I take the liberty of believing that it came as Gus Grissom would have wanted it to come, aboard his own spacecraft, still probing for more answers to the mysteries of space, which has, as he once wrote, "no horizons." He died in the splendid company of two men he admired and respected, and even in death he moved this country closer to the moon with spacecraft improvements designed to prevent a repetition of the tragedy that took his life.

Gus and Roger Chaffee were buried with full military honors in Arlington National Cemetery. Ed White lies in the military cemetery of his Alma Mater, the United States Military Academy at West Point, New York.

The final form of this book was reached with the approval of Mrs. Betty Grissom.

JACOB HAY

# A General Glossary of Space Terms

While many of these terms do not appear in this book, they occur frequently in accounts of space activities and are included here as a service to the reader.

**Ablating Materials**   Special heat-dissipating materials on the surface of a spacecraft that can be sacrificed (carried away, vaporized) during re-entry.

**Ablation**   Melting of ablative heat shield materials during re-entry of spacecraft into earth's atmosphere at hypersonic speeds.

**Abort**   The cutting short of an aerospace mission before it has accomplished its objective.

**Acceleration**   The rate of change of velocity. Decrease in velocity is sometimes called "negative acceleration."

**Acceptance Test**   A test or series of tests to demonstrate that performance is within specified limits.

**Acquisition and Tracking Radar**   A radar set which searches for, acquires, and tracks an object by means of reflected radio frequency energy from the object, or tracks by means of a radio-frequency signal emitted by the object.

**Actuators**   Devices which transform an electrical signal into a mechanical motion using hydraulic or pneumatic power.

**Adapter Skirt**   A flange or extension of a stage or section that provides a ready means of fitting another stage or section to it.

**Aerodynamic Heating**   The rise in the skin temperature of a vehicle due to the friction of the air at high speed.

**Aft-Firing Thrusters**   These are directed out the large end of the spacecraft. Their effect on the orbit path depends on the orientation of the spacecraft when they are fired.

**Airborne Data**   Data obtained from space systems during flight.

**Ambient**   Environmental conditions such as pressure or temperature.

**Analog Computer**   A computing machine that works on the principle of measuring, as distinguished from counting, in which the measurements obtained, as voltages, resistances, etc., are translated into desired data.

**Apogee**   The point at which a moon or artificial satellite in its orbit is farthest from the object it is orbiting.

**Asteroid**   One of the many thousands of minor planets which revolve around the sun, mostly between the orbits of Mars and Jupiter.

**Astrogation**   Navigating in space.

**Astronautics**   The art or science of designing, building, or operating space vehicles.

**Atmosphere**   The envelope of gases which surrounds the earth and certain other planets.

**Attitude**   The position of an aerospace vehicle as determined by the inclination of its axes to some frame of reference, usually the earth's surface.

**Axis**   Any of three straight lines, the first running through the center of the fuselage lengthwise, the second at right angles to this and parallel to the horizontal airfoils, and the third perpendicular to the first two at their point of intersection (aircraft).

**Azimuth** An arc of the horizon measured between a fixed point (e.g., true north) and the vertical circle through the center of an object.

**Ballistic Trajectory** The curved portion of a vehicle trajectory traced after the propulsion force is cut off.

**Biosphere** That part of the earth and its atmosphere in which animals and plants live.

**Blackout**

1. A fadeout of radio communications due to environmental factors such as ionospheric disturbances, or a plasma sheath surrounding a reentry vehicle.

2. A condition in which vision is temporarily obscured by a blackness, accompanied by a dullness of certain other senses, brought on by decreased blood pressure in the head and a consequent lack of oxygen, as may occur in any high g-force condition.

**Blip** A spot of light or other indicator on a radar scope (cathode-ray tube).

**Blockhouse** (Also written "block house.") A reinforced-concrete structure, often built underground or partly underground, and sometimes dome-shaped, to provide protection against blast, heat, or explosion during rocket launchings or related activities; specifically, such a structure at a launch site that houses electronic control instruments used in launching a rocket.

**Boilerplate** A full-size mockup that has all of the mechanical characteristics of the true item but none of the functional features.

**Booster** An engine that assists the normal propulsive system of a vehicle or other system of a vehicle.

**Burnout** The point when combustion ceases in a rocket engine.

**Capsule**   A small pressurized cabin with an acceptable environment, usually for containing a man or animal for extremely high-altitude flights, orbital space flight, or emergency escape.

**Cavitation**   The rapid formation and collapse of vapor pockets in a flowing liquid under very low pressures; a frequent cause of serious structural damage to rocket components.

**Celestial Guidance**   The guidance of a vehicle by reference to celestial bodies.

**Celestial Mechanics**   The science that deals primarily with the effect of force as an agent in determining the orbital paths of celestial bodies.

**Center of Mass**   Commonly called the center of gravity, it is the point at which all the given mass of a body or bodies may be regarded as being concentrated as far as motion is concerned.

**Centrifugal Force**   A force which is directed away from the center of rotation.

**Centrifuge**   A large motor-driven apparatus with a long rotating arm used to produce centrifugal force.

**Centripetal Force**   A force which is directed toward the center of rotation.

**Checkout**   A sequence of operational and calibrational tests to determine the condition and status of a system.

**Chemical Fuel**   (1) A fuel that depends on a oxidizer for combustion or for development of thrust, such as liquid or solid rocket fuel, jet fuel, or internal-combustion-engine fuel. Distinguished from nuclear fuel. (2) An exotic fuel that uses special chemicals.

**Circular Velocity**   Critical velocity at which a satellite will move in a circular orbit; it is extremely difficult to attain because of the accuracy of control needed.

**Closed Loop**   Automatic control units linked together with a process to form an endless chain.

**Closed Respiratory Gas System**   A completely self-contained system within a sealed cabin, capsule, or spacecraft that will provide adequate oxygen for breathing, maintain adequate cabin pressure, and absorb the exhaled carbon dioxide and water vapor.

**Cluster**  Two or more engines bound together so as to function as one propulsive unit.

**Command**  A pulse or signal initiating a step or sequence.

**Complex**  Entire area of launch site facilities. This includes blockhouse, launch pad, gantry, etc. Also referred to as a "launch complex."

**Condensation Trail (Contrails or Vapor Trails)**  A visible cloud streak, usually brilliantly white in color, which trails behind a vehicle in flight under certain conditions; caused by the formation of water droplets or sometimes ice crystals due to sudden compression, then expansive cooling, of the air through which the vehicle passes, and of introduction of water vapors through condensation of certain fuels.

**Configuration**  A particular type of a specific spacecraft, rocket, etc., which differs from others of the same model by virtue of the arrangement of its components or by the addition or omission of auxiliary equipment, as "long-range configuration."

**Console**  Term applied to a grouping of controls, indicators, and similar electrical or mechanical equipment.

**Control Rocket**—A rocket used to guide, accelerate, or decelerate a launch vehicle or spacecraft.

**Control System**  A system that serves to maintain attitude stability during forward flight and to correct deflections.

**Cosmic Rays**  Extremely fast particles continually entering the upper atmosphere from interstellar space; atomic nuclei which have very great energies because of their enormous velocities; potentially dangerous to life during extended exposure.

**Countdown**  The time period in which a sequence of events is carried out to launch a rocket; the sequence of events.

**Cryogenics**  The branch of physics that deals with temperatures below about —50 degrees C. More generally, cryogenics or its synonym cryogery refers to methods of producing very low temperatures.

**Damping**  Restraining.

**Destruct**  The deliberate action of detonating or otherwise destroying a missile or other vehicle after launch.

**Digital Computer**  A computer in which quantities are represented numerically and which can be used to solve complex problems.

**Dosimeter**  An instrument that measures the amount of exposure to nuclear or X-ray radiation; also called an intensitometer or dosage meter.

**Drag**  The aerodynamic force in a direction opposite to that of flight and due to the resistance of the body to motion in air.

**Entry Corridor**  The final flight path of the spacecraft before and during earth re entry.

**Environment**  An external condition or the sum of such conditions, in which a piece of equipment or a system operates, as in "temperature environment," "vibration environment," or "space environment." Environments are usually specified by a range of values, and may be either natural or artificial.

**Escape Orbit**  One of various paths that a body or particles escaping from a central force field must follow in order to escape.

**Escape Velocity**  The speed a body must attain to overcome a gravitational field, such as that of earth; the velocity of escape at the earth's surface is 36,700 feet per second.

**Exhaust Stream**  The stream of gaseous, atomic, or radiant particles that emit from the nozzle of a rocket or other reaction engine.

**Explosive Bolts**  Bolts surrounded with an explosive charge which can be activated by an electrical impulse.

**Extension Skirt**  Adapter used to connect elements of the spacecraft.

**Extravehicular**  Indicates that an element, such as an antenna, is located outside the vehicle.

**Fairing**  A piece, part, or structure having a smooth, streamlined outline, used to cover a nonstreamlined object or to smooth a junction.

**Final Trim**  Action that adjusts a vehicle to the exact direction programmed for its flight.

**Flash Point**  The temperature at which the vapor of a fuel or oil will flash or ignite momentarily.

**Flotation Collar**  A collar located around the spacecraft used to keep the spacecraft upright in the water and prevent sinking.

**Forward-Firing Thrusters**  Maneuvering rockets directed toward the nose of the spacecraft. When fired, these thrusters push the vehicle aft. This constitutes retrograde burn only if the vehicle is aimed SEF (small end forward) along its orbital path.

**Free-Return Trajectory**  A return to earth without power; this trajectory would be used in the event of a failure of the spacecraft propulsion system.

**Fuel Cell**  An electrochemical generator in which the chemical energy from the reaction of air (oxygen) and a conventional fuel is converted directly into electricity.

**G or G Force**  Force exerted upon an object by gravity or by reaction to acceleration or deceleration, as in a change of direction: one G is the measure of the gravitational pull required to move a body at the rate of about 32.16 feet per second.

**Gantry**  A frame structure that spans something, as an elevated platform that runs astride a work area, supported by wheels on each side; specifically, short for "gantry crane" or "gantry scaffold."

**Gimbal**  Mechanical frame containing two mutually perpendicular intersecting axes of rotation (bearing and/or shafts).

**Gimballed Motor**  A rocket motor mounted on gimbal; i.e., on a contrivance having two mutually perpendicular axes of rotation, so as to obtain pitching and yawing correction moments.

**Gravitation**   Force of attraction that exists between all particles of matter everywhere in the universe.

**Gravity**   That force which tends to pull bodies toward the center of mass; that is, to give bodies weight.

**Gravity Stimulation**   Use of centrifugal force to simulate weight reaction in a condition of free fall.

**Guidance System**   A system which measures and evaluates flight information, correlates this with target data, converts the result into the conditions necessary to achieve the desired flight path, and communicates this data in the form of commands to the flight control system.

**Guidance Tapes**   Magnetic or paper tapes that are placed in the computer and on which there previously has been entered information needed in guidance.

**Gyroscope**   A device consisting of a wheel so mounted that its spinning axis is free to rotate about either of two other axes perpendicular to itself and to each other; once set in rotation, its axle will maintain a constant direction, even when the earth is turning under; when its axle is pointed due north, it may be used as a gyro compass.

**Hold**   During a countdown: to halt the sequence of events until an impediment has been removed or function performed.

**Hypergolic**   Refers to bipropellant combinations which ignite spontaneously upon contact or mixing.

**Ice Frost**   A thickness of ice that gathers on the outside of a rocket vehicle over surfaces supercooled by liquid oxygen inside the vehicle.

**Incidence Angle**   The angle between earth and the path of a vehicle.

**Inertia**   The tendency of an object to remain put or if moving to continue on in the same direction.

**Inertial Guidance**   A sophisticated automatic navigation system using gyroscopic devices, etc., for high-speed vehicles. It absorbs and interprets such data as speed, position, etc., and automatically adjusts the vehicle to a predetermined flight path. Essentially, it knows where it's going and where it is by knowing where it came from and how it got there. It does not give out any signal so it cannot be detected by radar or jammed.

**Inertial Orbit** The type of orbit described by all celestial bodies, according to Kepler's laws of celestial motion. This applies to all satellites and spacecraft provided they are not under any type of propulsive power, their driving force being imparted by the momentum at the instant propulsive power ceases.

**Injection** The process of injecting a spacecraft into a calculated orbit. Also "insertion."

**Interface** A common boundary between one component and another.

**Interplanetary Space** That part of space conceived, from the standpoint of the earth, to have its lower limit at the upper limit of translunar space, and extending to beyond the limits of the solar system several billion miles.

**Intersteller Flight** Flight between stars; strictly, flight between orbits around the stars.

**Intersteller Space** That part of space conceived, from the standpoint of the earth, to have its lower limit at the upper limit of interplanetary space, and extending to the lower limits of intergalactic space.

**Inverter** A device that changes DC current to AC, or vice versa.

**Jet Steering** The use of fixed or movable jets on a space vehicle, ballistic missile, or sounding rocket to steer it along a desired trajectory, during both propelled flight (main engines) and after thrust cutoff.

**Launch Pad** The load-bearing base or platform from which a rocket vehicle is launched. Usually called "pad."

**Launch Vehicle** Any device which propels and guides a

spacecraft into orbit about the earth or into a trajectory to another celestial body. Often called "booster."

**Launch Window**  An interval of time during which a rocket can be launched to accomplish a particular purpose.

**Liftoff**  The action of a rocket vehicle as it separates from its launch pad in a vertical ascent. A liftoff is applicable only to vertical ascent; a takeoff is applicable to ascent at any angle. A liftoff is action performed by a rocket; a launch is action performed upon a  rocket or upon a satellite or spaceship carried by a rocket.

**Liquid Hydrogen (LH$_2$)**  A liquid rocket fuel that develops a specific impulse, when oxidized by liquid oxygen, ranging between 317 and 364 seconds depending upon the mixture ratio.

**Liquid Oxygen (LOX)**  Oxygen supercooled and kept under pressure so that its physical state is liquid.

**Loxing**  Vernacular term for the task of loading liquid oxygen into fuel tanks of a missile from a ground supply.

**Lunar Gravity**  The attraction of particles and masses towards the gravitational center of the moon.

**Mach**  (After Ernst Mach, 1858–1916. Austrian physicist.) A unit of speed measurement for a moving object equal to the speed of sound in the medium in which the object moves.

**Mass**  A measure of the quantity of matter in a body.

**Module**

1. A self-contained unit of a launch vehicle or spacecraft which serves as a building block for the overall structure. The module is usually designated by its primary function as "command module," "lunar landing modude," etc.

2. A one-package assembly of functionally associated electronic parts; usually a plug-in unit.

**Moon**  The natural celestial body that orbits as a satellite above the earth, revolving around it about once every 29½ days, reflecting the sun. The moon's mean distance from the earth is about 238,857 miles. The moon's diameter is about 2160 miles and its mass about 1/81 that of earth and the volume about 1/49. Its mean velocity is about 2285 statute miles per hour, its apogee 252,710 miles, perigee 221,463 miles.

**Nose Cone** The shield that fits over, or is, the nose of an aerospace vehicle.

**Orbit**

1. The path of a body or particle under the influence of a gravitational or other force. For instance, the orbit of a celestial body is its path relative to another body around which it revolves.
2. To go around the earth or other body in an orbit.

**Orbital Period** The interval between successive passages of a satellite over the same earth longitude.

**Orbital Velocity**

1. The average velocity at which an earth satellite or other orbiting body travels around its primary.
2. The velocity of such a body at any given point in its orbit, as in "its orbital velocity at the apogee is less than at the perigee."

**Oxidizer** In a rocket propellant, a substance such as liquid oxygen or nitric acid that yields oxygen for burning the fuel.

**Perigee** The point at which a moon or an artificial satellite in its orbit is closest to the object it is orbiting.

**Pitch** Displacement of rocket or spacecraft from its lateral axis.

**Pitchover** The programmed turn from the vertical that a rocket under power takes as it describes an arc and points in a direction other than vertical.

**Posigrade Burn** A rocket burn that adds forward energy along the orbital path. This raises the orbit 180° from the point of the burn.

**Posigrade Rocket** An auxiliary rocket which fires to augment the velocity of a vehicle, used for example in separating two stages of a vehicle.

**Propellant** A liquid or solid state mixture of fuel and oxidizer, and sometimes an additive, which when ignited in a combustion chamber changes into gases with a large increase in pressure and provides energy for thrust.

**Pressure Suit**   A garment designed to provide the human body with an environment above ambient pressure so that the respiratory and circulatory functions may continue normally, or nearly so, under low pressure conditions, such as occur at high altitudes or in space without benefit of a pressurized cabin.

**Radio Command**   A radio signal to which a guided missile, or the like, responds.

**Real Time**   Time in which reporting on events or recording of events is simultaneous with the events. For example, the real time of a satellite is that time in which it simultaneously reports its environment as it encounters it; the real time of a computer is that time during which it is accepting data.

**Reentry**   The event occurring when a spacecraft or other object comes back into the sensible atmosphere after being rocketed to altitudes above the sensible atmosphere; the action involved in this event.

**Remaining Body**   That part of a missile or other vehicle that remains after the separation of a fallaway section or companion body.

**Redundant**   A second means for accomplishing a given task. Also "back-up."

**Retrograde Impulse**   The impulse employed to slow a spacecraft or vehicle by applying a thrust in an opposite direction from the direction of motion of the spacecraft.

**Retrograde Motion**   Orbital motion opposite in direction to that normal to spatial bodies within a given system.

**Retrorocket**   A rocket that gives thrust in a direction opposite to the direction of an object's motion.

**Reverse Thrust**   Thrust applied to a moving object in a direction opposite to the direction of the object's motion.

**Roll**   The movements of a space vehicle about its longitudinal (X) axis.

**Scrub** To cancel out a scheduled launch either before or after countdown.

**Sensible Atmosphere** That part of the atmosphere that offers resistance to a body passing through it.

**Sensor** A sensing element. In a navigational system, that portion which perceives deviations from a reference and converts them into signals.

**Space Environment** The environment encountered by vehicles and living creatures upon entry into space.

**Space-Fixed Reference** An oriented reference system in space independent of earth phenomena for positioning.

**Space Platform** Large satellite with both scientific and military applications, conceived as a habitable base in space.

**Step Rocket** A rocket with two or more stages.

**Subsonic** Speed less than that of sound.

**Sustainer Rocket** A rocket engine used as a sustainer, especially on an orbital glider or orbiting spacecraft that dips into the atmosphere at its perigee.

**Telemetering** A system for taking measurements within an aerospace vehicle in flight and transmitting them by radio to a ground station.

**Thrust**

1. The propulsive force developed by an aircraft engine or a rocket engine.

2. Specifically, in rocketry, the product of propellant mass flow rate and exhaust velocity relative to the vehicle.

**Thrust Vector** The directional line of thrust of the spacecraft.

**Transistor** An electronic device that controls an electron current by the conducting properties of germanium or like material.

**Translational Control** A joystick located in the crew compartment to enable the pilot to control flight.

**Transponder** A radio transmitter-receiver which transmits identifiable signals automatically when the proper interrogation is received.

**Tumbling**  An unsatisfactory attitude situation in which a vehicle continues on its flight, but turns end over end about it center of gravity with its longitudinal axis remaining in the plane of flight.

**Ullage**  The volume in a closed tank or container above the surface of a stored liquid. Also the ratio of this volume to the total volume of the tank.

**Umbilical Cord**  A cable fitted to a vehicle with a quick-disconnect plug, through which electrical power, oxygen, etc., is transmitted.

**Weightlessness**

1. A condition in which no acceleration, whether of gravity or other force, can be detected by an observer within the system in question.

2. A condition in which gravitational and other external forces acting on a body produce no stress, either internal or external, in the body.

   Any object falling freely in a vacuum is weightless, thus an unaccelerated satellite orbiting the earth is "weightless," although gravity affects its orbit. Weightlessness can be produced within the atmosphere in aircraft flying a parabolic flight path. Weightlessness occurs when gravity forces are exactly balanced by other forms of acceleration.

**Yaw**

1. The lateral rotational or oscillatory movement of an aircraft, rocket, or the like about a transverse axis.

2. The amount of this movement, i.e., the angle of yaw.

3. Displacement of a launch vehicle or spacecraft from its longitudinal axis.

**X Axis**  A designation for the longitudinal axis in a coordinate system of axes.

**Y Axis**  A designation for the lateral axis in a coordinate system of axes.

**Z Axis**  A designation for the vertical axis in a coordinate system of axes.

**Zero Gravity**  The complete absence of gravitational effects.

*Index*

# Index

| | | | | | |
|---|---|---|---|---|---|
| DEC. | BORMAN | 203 | 330 hrs. | 5,716,900 mi. | |
| GEMINI VII | James A. LOVELL, Jr. | | 35 min. 17 sec. | 205 + | |

DEC. 15-16, 1965
GEMINI VI
...300 mi.
...5 +

MAR. 16, 1966
GEMINI VIII
...150 mi.
...+

JUNE 3-6, 196...
GEMINI IX
...30 mi.
...+

JULY 18-21, 196...
GEMINI X
...70 mi.
...+

SEPT. 12-15, 196...
GEMINI XI
...30 mi.
...+

NOV. 11-15, 196...
GEMINI XII
...10 mi.
...+

APR. 23-24, 1967
SOYUZ-1
...114 mi.
...+ *